Nourishing Connections

The Healing Power of Food & Community

Cathryn Couch & JoEllen DeNicola

CERES COMMUNITY PROJECT

Library of Congress Cataloging-in-Publication Data is on file with the publisher.

ISBN 978-0-615-31431-0

Published by
The Ceres Community Project
PO Box 1562
Sebastopol, CA 95473

707·829·5833
www.CeresProject.org

We are especially grateful to the following donors and foundations for providing financial support for this project:
the Dennis and Carol Ann Rockey Fund of the Marin Community Foundation, the Kathy Kent and John Dolinsek Fund of the Community Foundation of Sonoma County, and Dru W. Argue.

Donations to support our work can be mailed to The Ceres Community Project, PO Box 1562, Sebastopol, CA 95473. To make donations online, please go to our website, www.ceresproject.org and use the Donate button available on the Donating page.

For more information or to order this book directly from the publisher, go to www.ceresproject.org

Designed by Kim Stuffelbeam, The Ceres Community Project, kim@ceresproject.org

Photography, Kim Stuffelbeam, The Ceres Community Project, kim@ceresproject.org, and
Rose DeNicola, The Ceres Community Project, srdoggy@gmail.com

Illustrations by Patricia Waters, www.creativeartstudio.com, and Anna Stuffelbeam

Taos Carrots 4 (opposite the Table of Contents) reprinted with permission of artist Sandy Eastoak, www.sandyeastoak.com. The original painting on page 203 reprinted with permission of artist Nancy Rossiter Hutchins.

Printed by Jano Graphics, Ventura, California, www.janographics.com

Printed on recycled paper with at least 20% post consumer waste content using low VOC vegetable-based inks and alcohol-free components.

The FSC label indicates that this book was printed following strict guidelines to provide products made from viable resources and to promote responsible stewardship of the world's forests. FSC certification is widely regarded as one of the most important initiatives of the last decade to promote responsible forest management worldwide.

Mixed Sources
Product group from well-managed forests and other controlled sources
www.fsc.org Cert no. SCS-COC-001075
© 1996 Forest Stewardship Council

Preparing food
is not just about
yourself and others,
it is about everything.

~ Shunryu Suzuki

HEALING · FOOD · YOUTH · COMMUNITY

CERES COMMUNITY PROJECT

Acknowledgements

Cathryn Couch
Executive Director

From Cathryn

Each of us is the product not only of the hundreds who have influenced us personally in our lifetime, but even more fundamentally of the entire universal unfolding and especially the unique four and a half billion year history of our planet. Our knowledge, perspective and wisdom has been evoked out of this rich and shared history.

That being said, there are a few specific people that I would like to thank for the enormous role they played in birthing The Ceres Community Project in general and this book in particular.

A deep gratitude to Sue Curry Shaffer and Megan Salkin for being the spark that lit the flame of Ceres and for the generous financial support which allowed me to focus so much of my time on launching the project. Thanks to Cherie Lippard, Judi Pereira and Kathleen Capella for holding the space for Ceres during its gestation and for your enormous belief in the idea and support of me during challenging moments. To everyone at Bread for the Journey for believing in the vision and for your vital early financial support, and a special gratitude to Dr. Nan Fuchs who continues to champion The Ceres Community Project everywhere she can. Thank you to Andy's Produce for funding something like our first 2,000 meals and making me feel like family. To Karin Seder and the folks at The Community Church of Sebastopol, thanks for taking our fledgling project under your wing and holding us until we were ready to fly. Thank you to Sydney Randazzo, Chris Brettingen and everyone at To Celebrate Life Breast Cancer Foundation for your kindness and encouragement and for understanding the profound difference that lovingly prepared and nourishing food can make during cancer treatment. To Greg Young, Jody Snyder & Noel Littlejohn, and Judy Pike for the early financial support that allowed Ceres to blossom, and for sustaining that support so we could focus on developing the programs rather than where the money was coming from. To Patti Stack for your courage in stepping into the chaos of the kitchen in those early days, for your partnership, and for making so much space for us at 330 S. Main Street. To John Dolinsek and Peter Hoberg for your commitment to our work, and to all the Santa Rosa Sunrise Rotarians for your incredible partnership over the past several years in delivering meals to our clients throughout Sonoma County. To the extraordinary board members and staff whose competence, passion, commitment and enthusiasm have carried The Ceres Community Project far beyond my original conception. To our clients, teen chefs, volunteers, farmers, food partners, business sponsors and donors who, day in and day out, weave together the threads of Ceres.

To chefs Lisa Rost, Rebecca Katz and Terry Walters whose paths I've been lucky enough to cross and whose culinary adventures and creations have been important cross-fertilizations for the recipes you'll find in this book.

Thanks Mom for the gift of growing up in a home where real food was cooked from scratch every day and for supporting and encouraging my early attempts in the kitchen. All those bake sales and dinner parties! And to my father who passed away in February 2009 from multiple myeloma, my deepest gratitude for always telling me that I could do anything I set my mind to and for modeling the persistence and integrity which has stood me in such good stead over the years.

To Jeff and Hadley, thank you for your unwavering belief in me and the vision for The Ceres Community Project, and for the insight, creativity, integrity and kindness you bring to the world. I love you both with all my heart.

From JoEllen

I give my thanks to those who helped create the *Nourishing Connections* cookbook. It's a tool that we hope will serve you, our community, with simple to create flavors that nurture health.

Gratitude is due to all those who have come to the Healing Foods Cooking Course and created these wonderful dishes, commenting, adjusting and sharing what works and doesn't when one is dealing with cancer, Lyme disease, diabetes, and other serious health issues.

My heartfelt thanks go to Lily Mazzarella, Elaine Weil, Rebecca Katz, Nana Fuchs, Sarah Bearden and Ed Baumann for providing your nutritional expertise when we needed it. And to Coya Steele Silverlake, thank you for encouraging the best writing that I could muster and for your time and humor when I was ready to cry!

My deepest appreciation to my beloved husband, Henry – for encouraging and supporting the work, for the amazing home with the most wonderful kitchen and gardens we now share with those learning to cook, and for the sincere critiques on new dishes.

I love you.

JoEllen DeNicola
Nutrition Director

Thank you to my children, Michael, Louis, Sam and Rose, for being the first taste testers and giving me your true opinions. A special hug goes out to Rose for cooking with me and the Ceres Community Project for the past two years. And to Sam for jumping into the Ceres kitchen this past summer and sticking with it! XO

To you Cathryn, a big squeeze for all you are, all you have brought forth, and all that will follow. Thank you for creating the space for this healing work to begin. Much love!!

From JoEllen & Cathryn

Patricia Waters, whose beautiful line drawings illustrate *Nourishing Connections*, provided the needed impetus when she offered to help us create a cookbook in gratitude for the meals she received as a Ceres Project client. Our recipe testers – Alison & Carol VonSternberg, Carmen Taylor, Chris Brettingen, Dee Parker, Kathy Dowdall, Lindee Reese, Maggie Gelosi, Patricia Waters, Rita Minkin, Robin Setchko and Sue Carrell – supplied invaluable feedback that helped us make the recipe instructions simpler and the final results even more delicious.

A special thanks to Patricia Waters, Nancy Hutchins and Sandy Eastoak who generously allowed us to reproduce their original artwork in the pages that follow. And to Ceres teen chef and photographer Rose DeNicola, thank you for your fabulous shots of the Healing Foods Cooking Course and for shooting the various images we needed to round out the book. Thanks to Karen Boga, Lindee Reese, Julie Stuffelbeam, Melody Stewart and Janet DePree for lending their editing and proof-reading expertise. Any errors that remain are completely our responsibility! And finally, to Monica Kamsvaag, for volunteering her sharp eye and design skills to help keep the project on timeline.

Our deepest gratitude to Kim Stuffelbeam whose hours of photographic and design work have made so many things possible, not the least of these the book you now hold in your hands.

Tros Carrots 4

Table of Contents

Taos Carrots 4
by artist and Ceres Project client Sandy Eastoak.

Read Sandy's story on page 11.

INTRODUCTION

How It All Started:
The World Works in Mysterious Ways

We are in the midst of one of the most profound transformations in human history. Amidst global economic crisis, rising violence among nations, and a deepening awareness of the breakdown of the planet's ecosystems, a tidal wave of change is sweeping through communities everywhere.

The change is coming not from governments or political leaders, not from the United Nations, World Bank or International Monetary Fund. It's coming from people like you and me who are looking around our towns, neighborhoods and villages and seeing not just problems but opportunities. Often there is nothing more than the spark of an idea and the willingness of one or two or ten people to dive in and begin.

The Ceres Community Project's story is just one example. It all started quite innocently. At the time, I was dividing my time between two of my passions – working part-time as a chef at a retreat center in the western hills of Sonoma County and teaching horseback riding and training dressage horses at a farm in Santa Rosa. After spending ten years running a home-delivered meal service, I was enjoying the simplicity of getting paid for my work and not having to take it home with me.

On a lovely June day in 2006, I was driving to the barn when my cell phone rang. Sue Curry, my riding instructor, wondered if I could give her daughter a job over the summer and perhaps teach her to cook at the same time. There was no easy solution. I wasn't in a position to hire anyone – and who takes someone who can't cook on a catering job? But Sue was persistent and I have always been more inclined to say yes than no when the universe comes calling.

One conversation led to another and a couple weeks later I suddenly thought about a friend whom I knew was involved in the local cancer support community. One call confirmed that, yes, there were definitely families who could use help with meals. Sue offered to pay for the food, I donated my time, and Megan and I began meeting one afternoon a week to prepare meals for two single people and a family of four – all of them dealing with cancer or other serious health issues.

As Megan and I cooked together, I talked about my love of working with food. She gained confidence chopping and dicing and moved on to blanching and sautéing. Every afternoon, we packaged the food we'd made, creating grocery bags of meals for our three families. One of the first times that we cooked, the husband of a woman with breast cancer stopped to pick up their food on his way home from work. I had never met him before and introduced myself and Megan. We told him about the food we had prepared. I witnessed Megan's pride in the contribution she was making in their life and his deep gratitude for the simple gift of the meals. Something about that moment took hold in me.

Several weeks later, I woke early in the morning with a vision of a non-profit that would bring young people into the kitchen to learn to cook and eat healthy foods and then provide meals to individuals and families who were touched by serious illness. I wanted more people to benefit from what Megan and our three families were experiencing.

What prompted Sue to call me that day? When the idea entered my mind to call the friend who was involved in the cancer support community – where did that come from? And the vision of this as a non-profit, whose idea was that?

The Ceres Community Project's story is filled with seemingly inexplicable moments, connections, ideas and conversations. An expert in Quickbooks shows up to volunteer just as we've filed our incorporation papers and need to create our own accounting system. Someone passes a brochure to a local reporter in a moment when we are expanding. She writes a full-page story and we benefit from a needed influx of volunteers. A professional chef just happens to wander into an event we are catering as a fundraiser, picks up our brochure and calls me – a month before we are adding our second cooking day and I'm scrambling for help.

Over the past three years I've deepened my understanding of the energy or spirit at work in the universe. When we are able to open ourselves to its magic, when we learn to be attentive to where it is leading us – not just to our own plans and ideas – amazing things can happen. Today, The Ceres Community Project is truly the co-creation of hundreds of people, each of whom said "yes" in a moment of awareness that they had something to contribute, that there was a role to play in something larger.

That first morning when I "saw" what would become The Ceres Community Project, I remember being filled with excitement. The vision was very clear and I sensed an elegance to it – the way that it addressed so many needs in the community and so many things that I cared deeply about. Young people would learn to cook. People who needed healing food would have it. We would help teach people about the link between what we eat and our health. And we'd help to

"If we forget to play, we lose our love for life, and loving life is what will save our world, not fearing destruction. We're desperate to be invited into our joy, into our energy source, the belly laugh, the burst of giggles, wild abundance, bright color and zest for life of play. The laughing Buddha is fat to show that even the most massive bulk can lift off the ground – with a big enough laugh. Laughter is the sound of play and a doorway into play. Right now, wherever you are, put this article down and laugh. Not because there's anything funny going on, but because you're free to laugh. It may seem awkward at first, but stretch into it. Get off your spot. You will discover that you can find ecstasy just by moving toward it. Play is the movement of love, and love is what moves the Universe. Never underestimate, especially during a time of crisis, the power of play to move the world. Indeed it's the only thing that ever did."

—Gwen Gordon,
  "Play is the Movement of Love"

restore the idea of caring for our neighbors, something that had been lost between my parents' generation and my own.

Despite what I thought I understood, I can look back now and tell you that I barely had a clue about what the universe had in mind when it planted the idea for Ceres. Today, the project continues to unfold in ways that surprise me – and I imagine that a year or two from now, we will still be discovering more about how the heart of The Ceres Community Project wants to express itself.

Let me share a bit of the story of how we got from the idea to the reality.

Getting Off the Ground: Angels and Perseverance

During the fall after Megan and I had cooked together, I began talking in earnest with a few friends that were interested in the idea. If we were going to move forward, I wanted there to be a base of support beyond just myself. I also made lists of people who I believed would be supportive and who brought skills and/or knowledge that would help. While surprisingly few of them stepped up to the plate, unexpected help came from other directions.

A dear friend, Cherie Lippard – the person who I called that first morning when the idea appeared – heard about a group called Bread for the Journey which provided small grants to local non-profits. She gave me a copy of their brochure and I promptly sent them an email outlining the idea. The group was interested and a meeting was arranged for Cherie and me to talk with three members of the group's board at a local coffee shop. It was one of many small turning points in our journey. Based on the idea that local communities house the resources to solve local problems, Bread for the Journey looks for individuals with good ideas who have the skill, passion and support to make them a reality.

After talking for a half hour or so, the three women asked Cherie and I to move to another table. They conferred for a few minutes and then invited us back. With little fanfare, the group offered us the $1,000 we had asked for. The money was given without paperwork, with no strings attached. Their faith in what we were doing – and their willingness to put this small sum of money behind it – is one of the things that kept us going during those first sometimes challenging months.

I believed strongly that The Ceres Community Project needed to be owned by the community and that we would accomplish that by having as many people and businesses participating as possible – beginning with the local food markets. I started with Andy's Produce, a small locally owned grocery where I had shopped for many years. I had met one of the women who worked there several years earlier when we both boarded horses at the same barn.

I knew that Julie was part of the family who owned the store and stopped in one day to talk with her. We stood in the sun surrounded by huge bins of vegetables while I told her about my idea to bring young people into the kitchen and provide meals for people who were sick. I needed money for food, could Andy's help? She asked how much I wanted and the number $5,000 came out of my mouth. Julie offered to speak with her parents, the store owners, but warned me that they gave a lot of money to many different community causes and that the decision would be theirs.

A few weeks later, she told me that they had agreed to give me the full amount – even though we hadn't yet cooked a meal. When it went so smoothly at Andy's, I mistakenly thought it would be just as easy to raise this kind of money from every grocery store in town. When others didn't return my calls, or pledged much smaller amounts, I began to discover what an unprecedented gift Andy's had given us. When they reduced their support to $1,000 the following year, I realized that Andy's owners had played a vital role in launching The Ceres Community Project by providing enough money to allow us to demonstrate the idea.

Today, we maintain an account at Andy's and shop there weekly. We also order all of our bulk supplies through the store at significant savings, a way that the market continues to support our work.

We had our start-up capital and money for food. We had teens who wanted to cook with us, and there was no shortage of families needing the support of prepared meals. The two missing pieces were a commercial kitchen and a non-profit to house the project.

Cherie and I had put the word out that we were looking for a kitchen, but nothing had materialized. The ones we had looked at were much too small for an active group of teens, or were situated in places where noise was a concern. I knew we couldn't work freely and creatively with young people and worry about noise!

We had been thinking about church kitchens when someone mentioned The Community Church of Sebastopol, a sprawling network of buildings at the north end of town. Finding a location where we could cook was clearly critical and we seemed to be hitting dead ends wherever we turned. It was with this feeling of frustration that I walked into the church office and meet Karin Seder, the church's facilities manager. Karin and I had spoken briefly on the phone, but it was in our first in-person meeting that I really felt Karin's – and the church community's – support. She told me that

"I cannot tell you how much the meals you made for me meant. Not only were they beautiful and tasty, but eating them made me feel like all the love and support the universe has was coming directly to me from you through the food you sent. That positive response you participated in makes healing seem certain."
— Rita

"This service is amazing and I can actually feel the difference. It encourages me to eat healthier. I'm generally too tired to eat healthy. Thanks to all of you!"
— Barbara

"I find The Ceres Community Project touches me beyond words. The many young people who prepare the meals give so much of themselves. I look forward to unveiling each week's creations, always so fresh, tasty and inviting. It helps so much to know that people, beyond family and friends, actually care and wish to ease my path to recovery. A heartfelt thank you to each and every one."
— Linda

"Wow! My first delivery of food came today, and I was blown away at how good the food is! My appetite has been so minimal that I have been forcing myself to eat, but your menu was so fresh, healthy and good that I know I will love this program, and look forward to the deliveries."
— Patty

the church had two kitchens that might work for us and promptly took me around to see them.

When we walked into the main kitchen, which shared a building with a basketball court (no worries about noise here!), I knew we had found our home. The kitchen was square with a large island in the middle where at least six people could work. There was a commercial refrigerator, six burner stove, gas and convection ovens, a commercial dishwasher and a good assortment of pots and pans. Karin told me that the kitchen was available and she agreed to let us use it one afternoon a week for a small donation of $100 a month to help cover utilities and wear and tear.

By the middle of October, we had funds from Bread for the Journey to cover the insurance that the church required along with some cooking equipment and containers, we had a line of credit at Andy's Produce to pay for food, and we had a kitchen. The one stumbling block was a non-profit partner so that we could solicit donations and apply for grants. After being strung along for three months without a decision, we walked away from our first potential partner. It was a hard lesson and enormously frustrating. Thinking that we had found a perfect match, we had stopped looking for other possibilities, ending up losing time and wasting energy.

In early January of 2007, we cut our losses and began seeking a new partner. One of our Bread for the Journey angels, Dr. Nan Fuchs, introduced us to Dr. Terri Turner, a local osteopath who also ran a small non-profit with the goal of improving the quality of patient care by increasing communication and respect among practitioners. Terri and I spoke for about an hour on the phone and then met for lunch. From her own experience with patients, Terri saw the enormous benefit of what we were hoping to do. She agreed to present the idea to her board. Unfortunately, there wasn't another board meeting until mid-February. I was going to have to be patient.

Right about the same time, we learned about a group in Marin that was funding projects that supported men and women with breast cancer. My first thought was that we shouldn't apply. While two of the people Megan and I had cooked for had breast cancer, I wanted The Ceres Community Project to be available to a broader range of people. After a number of conversations with To Celebrate Life Breast Cancer Foundation and a few of the people working with me on The Ceres Community Project, we decided to apply for a grant, agreeing to use the funds specifically for breast cancer survivors. The only problem was that we couldn't apply for a grant without a non-profit partner.

On Thursday, February 8th, I met with the board of Relationship Centered Community Care and explained the idea for Ceres and the resources we had put in place. The next morning, Terri told me that the board had agreed to sponsor us. The grant for To Celebrate Life was due by noon the following day in Marin County, about an hour and a half away! I wrote the grant on Friday, drove to a copy shop in Marin on Saturday morning to make the required number of copies, and delivered it to the head of the grants committee an hour before the noon deadline.

In mid-March, To Celebrate Life called to let us know they had awarded us a $7,500 grant to provide meals to breast cancer clients. Finally, on March 29, 2007, The Ceres Community Project got off the ground. Three high school students from Summerfield Waldorf School and one student from El Molino High School in Forestville gathered with me at The Community Church's kitchen to prepare meals for four local families.

The details of those early months run together for me now. Here's what I remember. Laughter and something just below total chaos in the kitchen. Days with too few teen helpers and days with too many. Heartfelt notes of thanks from our clients. Demonstrating how to chop an onion, sauté shiitakes and blanch broccoli. Prepping yet another case of kale. Driving food to a client when a delivery volunteer didn't show up at the kitchen. The enormity of packing every single thing we needed and taking it all to the kitchen – then having to return it all home again at the end of the day.

Not Quite It: Untapped Potential and More Angels

Those first six months I wavered between absolute commitment to what we were doing and frustration at its limitation. We were clearly making a difference, yet almost everything we were doing fell short of what I saw the potential to be. I was still working at another job and putting all of my free time into Ceres but it felt harried and disorganized.

I wanted the experience to be richer and more meaningful for the teens. I wanted to make the program available to more people. I imagined what it would be like to have all of our food grown by local farmers and a kitchen where we could store all of our ingredients, allowing us more freedom to create on the spot. There was so much possibility yet it was taking all of my free time just to get the weekly cooking done and out to the clients.

That October I found myself at the Bioneers Conference in Marin County. If you haven't heard of it, the Bioneers annual conference is one of the more inspiring experiences on the planet. Some 3,000 people from across the globe gather to share practical solutions to

"It is especially important in this discussion to recognize the unity of the total process, from that first unimaginable moment of cosmic emergence through all its subsequent forms of expression until the present. This unbreakable bond of relatedness that makes of the whole a universe becomes increasingly apparent to scientific observation, although this bond ultimately escapes scientific formulation or understanding. In virtue of this relatedness, everything is intimately present to everything else in the universe. Nothing is completely itself without everything else. This relatedness is both spatial and temporal. However distant in space or time, the bond of unity is functionally there. The universe is a communion and a community. We ourselves are that communion become conscious of itself."

– Thomas Berry

the world's most pressing problems. During the afternoon, I sat in the main plenary hall listening to Joanna Macy, Jean Shinoda Bolen, Alice Walker and several other women leaders. They were talking honestly and directly about the state of the planet. As I sat listening, I wrote on my pad, "what would it look like if I took The Ceres Community Project on wholeheartedly?"

I knew I was holding myself back and I also knew that if I was going to dive in, I needed to free up more time. That meant finding a way to pay myself at least a small amount so that I could let go of other work.

Three days later, I happened to be visiting with a friend of a friend whose partner had died of breast cancer eight months before. After a bit, I began to tell her about the work we were doing with Ceres. By the time we parted, she had offered me $5,000 to help me pay myself. The next day, I had a meeting with a man who had heard about what we were doing through someone at Bread for the Journey. Sitting across the table from one another at a small café in downtown Windsor, I told him how the project had come to be, what we had accomplished so far, and what I thought the potential might be. After about twenty minutes he asked, "How can I help?"

I admitted to him that I didn't really have any idea what he had in mind. I had simply heard that he was interested and had come to talk with him. He told me that he was a philanthropist and asked how much money I thought would make a difference? By the end of that half hour meeting, I had secured another $10,000 – funds that would allow me to make this work my priority.

That twenty-four hour period was one of the most profound experiences during The Ceres Community Project's early life. In that short period of time, everything had shifted.

Those two donors sensed the possibility of The Ceres Community Project at this very early stage. By putting their faith and financial support behind our work, they were instrumental in unleashing the enormous potential that we were sitting with.

Over the next four months, the entire structure and operation of the organization changed. Volunteers showed up who were willing and able to take on major areas of responsibility. I brought together a small group as an advisory board and we began meeting monthly. We added a second cooking day, doubling the number of teens who could participate and creating the potential for doubling our client load as well. By March, just a year after the project began, we incorporated as our own non-profit and filed for 501(c)(3) status from the IRS. The Ceres Community Project was no longer a little project that I was doing on the side one day a week.

> *"The truth is that all aspects of the current crisis reflect the same mistake, setting ourselves apart and using others for our gain. So to heal one aspect helps the others to heal as well. Just find what you love to work on and take joy in that."*
>
> – Joanna Macy

Two Years and 32,000 Meals Later

During our first eight months in 2007, we provided about 4,500 meals to 28 different households cooking just one afternoon a week in our church kitchen. A year and a half after that first day, we moved to a new kitchen leased by long time volunteer Patti Stack. Patti launched her catering business Capers & Company and provided space for The Ceres Community Project three afternoons a week. We now had a home where we could store our growing amount of food, containers and equipment. Even more importantly, we had a space where we could bring our clients and their stories more present for our teen volunteers.

During 2008, we tripled the number of meals we provided to more than 17,300. By December of that year, at least 125 teens had participated in the program and we had nearly 100 active volunteers. Our client load had grown from 12 at the end of the previous year to 34 and we had begun to develop a nutrition education and cooking class program for clients who were ready to cook for themselves.

As we entered 2009, we were busy creating organizational charts, budgeting, writing goals, and hiring a small group of part-time staff. Another significant shift was in the works. Once again, The Ceres Community Project didn't look at all like it had a few months previously.

By the end of 2009, the Ceres Community Project will have provided 45,000 beautiful, delicious, nourishing and *free* meals to hundreds of local families. At least 250 young people will have worked in our kitchens with about 25 participating each week. Our 16 hour educational program, the Healing Foods Cooking Course, is being offered every other month, providing knowledge, skills and inspiration for those recovering from illness and their caregivers. A free Healing Foods lecture series extends our reach into the larger community.

2009 brought expanded connections with local farmers and food producers. Virtually all of our produce is now donated, coming from our local Whole Foods store, farms, school and community gardens, and the kitchen gardens of several local wineries. Our client offerings include specialty foods like our Immune Broth, Vitality Truffles and Arame Ginger Sauerkraut, some of which we also sell at our local farmer's market. And we are in conversation with people in neighboring Marin and Napa counties, Seattle and New Jersey about launching similar projects.

Thursday

1. Kamut Pasta w/ Roasted Butternut, Greens, Onions + White Beans
   * / w/ Rice

2. Curried Winter Vegies

3. Fish w/ Citrus Marinade   Cabbage + Carrots w/ Sesame

4. Package Pumpkin Mousse
   * 4 Flan

5. Package Radish Salad
   / Sauerkraut

The Importance of Remembering

During those early months of launching The Ceres Community Project we felt our way. What kind of food was helpful? How many meals could we cook in an afternoon with teen volunteers? How many teens could we have working before things tipped over into chaos? Could the teens help with delivery or was it too much to ask after a long day at school and time in the kitchen? What we knew was that there were local families that needed the support of lovingly prepared healing food, and that young people had much to give and much to gain by joining us in the kitchen.

The many questions that arose answered themselves as we moved forward. Today, despite the fact that our size and organizational structure have changed, the process continues to be the same. As we enter 2010, we have a sense of how we might deepen and expand our contribution here in Sonoma County and across the country. We have plans and goals and budgets for the year ahead. And yet we remain aware and attentive to what has not yet revealed itself. We know without a doubt that The Ceres Community Project will look different a year from now – and in ways that we cannot yet anticipate.

At its heart The Ceres Community Project is a force for creating connection and healing and for rediscovering the vast web of relationship in which we live. I can't take credit for the idea, nor can I take responsibility for what has been accomplished. I was simply open to what presented itself and willing to step in and begin. As I shared the vision with others, they brought new insights and helped to create more possibility.

Today, The Ceres Community Project is a co-creation of hundreds, perhaps thousands of people. So many strands have woven together – the experiences, needs and ideas of our many clients, teen and adult volunteers, business sponsors and referral agencies; the bounty and diversity of food which has come our way and the generosity of the farmers; the creativity of all the cooks throughout history; and on and on.

What Difference Does It Make: The Big Picture

Obviously, The Ceres Community Project is making a big difference in the lives of many people:

- Our clients receive beautiful and nourishing meals at a time of enormous stress and challenge. Many of them are economically disadvantaged, live alone, and could not afford the quality of food we provide without our service. Here in Sonoma County, and in many other places, there is no meal support unless you are elderly.

"I have two daughters, Tina, recently married and living in Rohnert Park, and Anaar, a medical student at Northwestern in Chicago. After I was treated by an emergency room doctor and my primary care physician for a blood pressure spike last December, Tina complained to Anaar that something didn't look right. Anaar brought her stethoscope and rubber hammer home for the holidays and found an eleven pound tumor both doctors had missed. Then she found an excellent surgeon at UCSF, Dr. Eric Nakakura, very experienced in excising retroperitoneal liposarcoma. Tina helped me find the Ceres Community Project, a great blessing in my long recovery. Not only is the food delicious, but I find special comfort in the role of young people in providing this vital service.

Thanks to my daughters, my mother, UCSF, Ceres, and many generous friends, I am returning to my work as a painter--with the renewed purpose that follows the heavy questions that are cancer's gift. I'm a member of Sebastopol Gallery, and my responsibilities there helped pull me back to health. The work I showed as featured artist this fall included many Native American elements. Now I'm collaborating with a Pomo dancer who liked these paintings on a project to represent Pomo life ways to the larger community.

Thank you Ceres Community Project for feeding me. Your nourishment will show in the paintings produced in this collaboration!"

– Sandy Eastoak

- Clients tell us that the meals they receive help them feel connected to and supported by the whole community – an enormous contribution to their healing.
- Our teen chefs develop culinary skills, gain an understanding of the link between what they eat and their health, and learn about leadership and team work. Even more fundamentally, they discover their own competence and the enormous satisfaction of contributing to their world.
- Those participating in our educational programs – the Healing Foods Cooking Course and lecture series – gain the knowledge, skills and inspiration to make whole foods a part of their lives.
- And all of us involved in Ceres, as clients, staff, board, teen chefs, volunteers, food donors and business sponsors, benefit from feeling connected and engaged in the larger world.

The Ceres Community Project is part of a growing movement to recover a healthy and nourishing relationship with our bodies, the food we eat, community, and the larger web of life which provides that food.

The western industrialized diet is at the root of an epidemic of obesity, diabetes, cancer, heart disease and auto-immune conditions that is ravaging our parents, friends, family members and children. Scientists now agree that fully 35 percent of all cancers could be prevented by eating a healthier diet. The statistics are similar for heart disease, and the relationship between poor quality diets and diabetes is much higher.

Beyond that, we have become increasingly disconnected from one another. More of us move away from our families than ever before and few of us stay at the same job for longer than a year or two. Church attendance is down as is participation in service clubs, bowling leagues and other forms of social networking. A 2006 study by the National Science Foundation found that 25 percent of Americans say that in times of personal crisis they have no one they can confide in, double the number in 1985.

Yet researchers are confirming that feeling connected and cared for contributes significantly to long-term health and to our capacity for healing. A 1997 Carnegie Mellon University study found that people with rich social networks were four times less likely to become ill than those with fewer friends.

The Ceres Community Project grew out of an understanding of these forces. Our mission is to restore whole, local and organically grown food to its place as the foundation of health for our bodies, communities and planet.

About this Cookbook

In the following pages we've tried to capture our current understanding about the kind of food that is most supportive of good health. We've paid special attention to the needs of those touched by serious illness, and have tried to provide information, recipes and resources to enable you to feed yourself well despite the challenges that illness presents.

The recipes that made it into the cookbook had to meet several rigorous criteria – 1) They had to include a high proportion of foods that are especially beneficial for health, 2) they had to be simple to make, 3) the end result needed to be delicious, and 4) at least in most cases, they needed to allow for variation and improvisation.

Our goal is simple – to encourage you – whether young or old, ill or well – to rediscover the joy and satisfaction of cooking. Food, as all indigenous people have known throughout history, is our "primary medicine". What we eat literally becomes us.

As research mounts, it's increasingly clear that we either support or burden our bodies based on the foods we choose to eat. While that may sound stark, think of it this way. Whole, organically grown foods are recognized by our bodies. We have the capacity to process, digest and put them to good use with a minimum of effort. These foods are building, restoring and nourishing.

Most processed foods are made up of chemically created ingredients which our bodies don't recognize as food and don't know how to process. They include a high proportion of toxic byproducts. Digesting these foods and eliminating the toxins puts enormous stress on our systems and takes energy away from healthy processes.

Cooking brings with it an enormous range of benefits. First and foremost, it allows you to take control over what you and those you love eat. If you don't cook, you are dependent on purchased food prepared by others. Often this food isn't as fresh or as whole as what you might make. In addition, it carries the energetic imprint of those who made it and whatever emotional state they were in. When you cook, you have the opportunity to imbue the food with love, gratitude and healing energy.

Cooking is empowering. When you prepare your own food, you send a message of love – that you care enough to take the time to prepare a healthy meal. When you cook, you have the pleasure of handling food directly. You get a chance to notice how beautiful and colorful it is. Through the food, you reconnect to the earth and tap into a deep well of gratitude for its sustenance.

Our Mission

To restore whole, local and organically grown food to its place as the foundation of health and healing for people, communities and the earth.

What We Do

- Provide delicious and nourishing whole foods meals and a community of support to individuals and families touched by life-threatening illness.

- Inspire young people to become life-long stewards of their world, and give them the understanding and skills to become advocates for whole, local and organically grown foods in their own lives and the lives of others.

- Educate the larger community about the relationship between what we eat and the health of our bodies, our communities and the earth, and provide the skills and inspiration for each of us to become advocates for positive change in our own lives and the lives of others.

> "Each of us is truly our primary doctor with nature as our guide. We have all the healing knowledge we need within our very beings. Learning to make contact with the healing ability within and using this knowledge in our daily life is the route to better and better health and well-being."
>
> – Elson Haas,
> *Staying Healthy with the Season*

> "Embedded in family life and in cultural and religious ritual, food has always been our most direct, intimate tie to a nurturing earth as well as a primary means of bonding with each other. Food has helped us to know where we are and who we are."
>
> – Frances Moore Lappe,
> *Hope's Edge*

Finally, cooking provides an opportunity to slow down and be present. In the midst of a busy day, fifteen minutes of washing and chopping vegetables can provide a deeply healing pause. Cooking calls you into *this* moment, requiring that you breathe, slow your pace, and pay attention to where you are and what you are doing.

If you don't cook, it may seem like a mysterious and complicated process. In fact, cooking is quite simple. At its heart, cooking is the marriage of two things: 1) learning a few basic techniques, and 2) discovering the kinds of foods that make both your taste buds and your body sing. If you need some help with the first part, take a look at the chapter called Getting Started. There you'll find definitions of basic cooking terms and a simple overview of the techniques you'll need for the recipes in this book.

The second is the part that no one can do for you. It's also the ultimate answer to developing a way of eating that is uniquely suited to and supportive of your physical, emotional and spiritual health. Begin with your own curiosity and be willing to let go of any preconceived ideas you have about what you like and don't like.

Before you eat, ask yourself what your body really wants and take the time to listen for the answer. After you eat, notice how you feel. Is your energy good and does it last? Do you feel clear or foggy? Do you sleep well at night and wake up feeling refreshed? Over time, this simple process will yield a rich understanding of the kind of food that is most suited to you in any given moment. You might keep a special journal to record what you discover.

As we've researched healing foods and cooked for people who are ill, we've discovered that there are a number of important foods that are unfamiliar to many people – fermented foods like sauerkraut, sea vegetables, seeds with Omega 3 oils such as chia and flax, sprouted foods and alternative sweeteners to name a few. In the next chapter, Nutrition Basics, we provide a general introduction to our philosophy about eating to support health, whether you are ill or well. You'll learn about foods you may not be familiar with, the importance of healthy fats and how to reduce or eliminate sugar from your diet. If you are currently dealing with illness, Nutrition Basics also provides tips for feeding yourself well when you have very little energy.

Finally, at the back of the book you'll find a Resource Guide to support you in exploring many of these topics in more detail. There are books, organizations and websites which we have found to be useful in understanding the role between what we eat and our health. We've also provided sources for hard to find ingredients.

The Ceres Community Project is a work in process – an ongoing collaboration that is being shaped by our clients, teen and adult volunteers, staff, board, business sponsors, farmers and the larger community in which we live and work. We hope that what we have shared here – our current best understanding of how we can eat to support our health – nourishes your body, mind and spirit and encourages you to cook and eat in accordance with your own deepest nature.

Blessings and bon appetit!

Cathryn

kale

In April, 2008, I had a radical cystectomy followed by chemotherapy. I live alone and often didn't feel like eating, much less cooking. Having healthy, delicious meals right in my refrigerator allowed me to eat even though I thought I didn't want to. Knowing the food was made with love and care nourished me as well, not to mention training teens to cook. What an incredible community resource!!!!

Patricia Waters

Chapter 1 • Nutrition Basics

Why Do We Call Food "Primary Medicine"?

What we eat – and are able to absorb – plays a fundamental role in our long-term health and in our ability to protect from and heal illness. Increasingly, scientists, researchers and health providers are recognizing this link between diet and health.

When you stop and think about it, this comes as no surprise. For tens of thousands of years, humans and our pre-human ancestors evolved interdependently with the plants, fungi and animals we found in our immediate environments. We learned how to make foods digestible through cooking and various forms of fermentation, but beyond that foods were as close to their whole form as possible. Only in the past hundred years have highly processed and chemically created foods become part of our diets. In our busy lives, we are turning more and more to "convenience" and take-out foods – many of which would be unrecognizable to our ancestors and are also unrecognizable to our bodies.

There is no one explanation for the epidemic of disease that we see happening all around us. Longer life spans, stress, lack of exercise and pollution in our environment all probably have a part to play. But the radical change in our eating habits and the stress this puts on our bodies is clearly one of the keys.

In *Foods to Fight Cancer*, scientists Richard Beliveau and Denis Gingras claim that 70 percent of all cancers can be avoided by factors that are under our control – by changing our diets, quitting smoking, maintaining a healthy weight and avoiding drugs and excess alcohol. Rather than thinking of cancer – and heart disease and diabetes – as something you don't have control over, we encourage you to discover that you can have enormous impact on your health by the choices you make every day.

Most American diets fall into one of two broad categories: "Western" or "prudent." The prudent diet is a nutritionist's dream. People in this category tend to eat [primarily] fish, poultry, cruciferous vegetables (i.e. cabbage and broccoli), greens, tomatoes, legumes, fresh fruits, and whole grains. They skimp on fatty or calorie-rich foods such as red meats,

"Human beings, after all, do not eat solely to live, they wish that life to be as long and as agreeable as possible. This quest for longevity has led humankind to seek benefits from food that are greater than nutritional value alone; food was the only available resource that could have positive effects on health and prolong existence. Therefore it should not be surprising that the history of medicine is bound up with that of food and diet; food, for a very long time, was humanity's only medicine."

– Foods to Fight Cancer

eggs, high-fat dairy products, French fries, pizza, mayonnaise, candy, and desserts.

The Western diet is the prudent diet reflected in a carnival mirror. Everything is backwards: Red meat and other fatty foods take the forefront, while fruits, vegetables, and whole grains are pushed aside. In addition to fat and calories, the Western diet is loaded with cholesterol, salt, and sugar. If that weren't bad enough, it's critically short on dietary fiber and many nutrients – as well as plant-based substances (phytochemicals) that help protect the heart and ward off cancer.   –"What's Wrong with the American Diet?"

The foods available to us today range widely in their effect on our health – from strongly supportive to virtually toxic. When we eat things that our body doesn't recognize (chemically created "low fat" foods for example), or too much of something that our body isn't used to from an evolutionary perspective (such as a lot of refined white sugar), it disturbs our body's balance. Valuable energy is spent trying to process and eliminate these foods and we lack the nutrients and phytochemicals we need for healthy functioning.

Eating a plant-based, whole foods and organic diet is the foundation for long-term health – this is why, at The Ceres Community Project, we call these foods "primary medicine".

This doesn't mean that you have to stick to a diet of organic brown rice and collard greens to be healthy! Our bodies are amazingly resilient and have the capacity to process some amount of refined sugars, alcohol, preservatives and so on. If you are basically healthy, sticking to the 80/20 rule will probably work for you – 80 percent of your diet coming from organic, plant-based whole foods and 20 percent not quite that nutrient-dense. If you are not at optimum health, however, we encourage you to eliminate most if not all of those foods that don't actively support your body – that includes all processed and refined foods, sugar in all its forms, alcohol and foods containing chemical preservatives.

As you'll discover in the recipes that follow, eating for health also doesn't mean that you have to sacrifice taste. At The Ceres Community Project we believe food must be beautiful, delicious *and* nutritious in order to be truly nourishing. Body, mind, soul and spirit are inextricably connected. When we feed our souls, our bodies are nurtured as well.

Here are a few facts about our current eating habits and their effect on our health:

- Americans in 2000 ate an average of 2,700 calories a day, up 24.5% or 530 calories per day from 1970. That equates to an additional 56 pounds of body weight per person per year.

- The increase comes from refined grains (9.5%), fats and oils (9.0%) and sugar (4.7%).

- The average American is eating 152 pounds of refined sugar per year – that's equivalent to more than 1 cup per person per day.

- Only 11% of Americans are eating the recommended 5 to 9 servings per day of fruit and vegetables – and this includes dried fruit and 100% fruit juice, potato chips and French fries, ketchup, pizza sauce and iceberg lettuce.

- More than half of our meals are now eaten away from home.

- 66% of adults are overweight and 27% are obese. One-third of all children are overweight.

- Estimates are that by 2012, one in three children will be diabetic.

- Cancer now affects one in three people before the age of 75 and one in four will die from complications caused by the disease.

- 52.5% of all deaths in the United States – from heart disease, cancer and diabetes – are directly related to the combination of poor nutrition, obesity and inactivity.

- An estimated one-third of the 565,650 cancer deaths expected in 2008 – or 188,000 – are believed to be directly related to diet, overweight or obesity, and/or physical inactivity.

> *"Think about it! When you breathe, you breathe the creations of a star. All the life you will live is possible because of the gifts of that star. Your life has been evoked through the work of the heavens…The air we breathe, the food we eat, the compounds out of which we are composed: all are creations of the supernova.*
>
> *When we deepen our awareness of the simple truth that we are here through the creativity of the stars, we begin to feel fresh gratitude. When we reflect on the labor required for our life, reverence naturally wells up within us. Then, in the deepest regions of our hearts, we begin to embrace our own creativity. What we bestow on the world allows others to live in joy."*
>
> – Brian Swimme,
> *The Universe is a Green Dragon*

Beyond the Physical Food-Health Connection

There is another way of looking at the food we eat that has nothing to do with how nutritious it is for our bodies, but might contribute just as much to our wholeness and long-term vitality. Food is our most fundamental connection to both ourselves and the world around us.

When we eat, we take in the energy of the cosmos formed over 14 billion years into the immense complexity of the plant and animal kingdoms… and that energy becomes us. Human existence stands on the evolutionary shoulders of the plants, beginning with the single-celled organisms that figured out how to take sunlight and turn it into energy. This giant leap – what we now call photosynthesis – changed the oxygen content of Earth's atmosphere and ultimately allowed for the development of mammals and eventually the human species.

Plants continue to be the only organisms that can grow directly from the combination of water and sunlight. All other species are dependent on them in some form for their existence – and we humans are ultimately the most dependent.

For the past four or five hundred years, we have held the false and damaging notions of human separateness and superiority. As scientific understanding broadens, we have come to realize our absolute connection and dependence on the rest of creation. Today, there is a growing conversation among scientists, cosmologists and spiritual leaders about what contribution humans might play in and for the larger whole of life. What is the role of humans? One suggestion, offered by Professor Brian Swimme, is that humans bring the capacity to reflect and celebrate life's magnificence, that it is our job to sing the praises of the rest of creation.

When we realize that we are literally given life through the gifts of the plant worlds, we come to food from a new and deeply grateful place. We understand that human life is possible because of the enormous creativity of plants over millions of years. When we walk through a farmers' market, we are touched by the abundance and generosity of the earth. When we sit down to eat, we understand that the food on our plate is the result of billions of years of the universe's unfolding, and that we, just like the plants and animals, are intricately interwoven into that creation.

What we eat becomes *us*. When we eat with awareness of the gift food is, we locate ourselves in the immense mystery of the creation. Gratitude springs naturally from this place and our lives are deepened and enriched by the knowing that we, too, have a place at the table.

The Basics:
Plant-Based, Whole Foods, Organic

If you pay attention to the news, it might seem like you need a Ph.D. to figure out how to eat. The truth is, it's actually quite simple. We'll explore some of the details in the sections that follow, but if you remember this simple phrase you'll be at least 90 percent of the way there: *plant-based, whole foods, organic*. What is so important about these three concepts?

A *Plant*-Based Diet Is the Key

While no single nutrient or food can protect against diseases such as cancer, plant foods contain the minerals, vitamins and phytochemicals that seem to interact to provide extra support for good health. The American Institute of Cancer Research recommends that at least ⅔ of your plate be filled with vegetables, fruits, whole grains and legumes – the plant foods.

A second benefit of a predominantly plant-based diet is that it helps protect against weight gain – a contributing factor for many health conditions. Plant foods are low energy dense, low calorie foods.

Rather than focus on a small number of plant foods, your best bet is to eat a wide variety of vegetables, fruits, grains and legumes including foods from the following categories:

- cruciferous vegetables including broccoli, cauliflower, Brussels sprouts and cabbage;
- dark leafy greens like kale, chard, collard greens, romaine lettuce and bok choy;
- deep orange and red vegetables like butternut and other winter squashes, yams, tomatoes, and red, yellow and orange bell peppers;
- fruits such as blueberries, red grapes, strawberries and raspberries, and citrus fruits such as oranges, lemons, limes and grapefruit;
- whole grains such as brown rice, millet, quinoa, barley, buckwheat, oats and amaranth;
- legumes such as lentils, split peas, aduki beans, navy beans, black beans, kidney beans and garbanzo beans.

Eat the rainbow every day and you'll include foods with a broad range of nutrients in your daily diet.

"The range of healthful nutrient intake is broad, and foods from the earth, tree, or animal can be combined in a seemingly infinite number of ways to create diets that meet health goals. The attention paid to single nutrients, to individual foods, and to particular diseases distracts from the basic principles of diet and health… you are better off paying attention to your overall dietary pattern than worrying about whether any one single food is better for you than another."

– **Marion Nestle**, *What to Eat*

The *Whole* Is Greater than the Sum of the Parts

In our overly scientific age, we've spent an enormous amount of time and energy trying to identify specific nutrients that can protect against disease. Today, scientists are starting to question this approach. The chemical constituents of plants are extremely complex. Garden thyme, for example, contains 38 different antioxidants that we know of. We are a long way from understanding how these components work together to produce a certain result, but we are beginning to realize that the whole is greater than the sum of the parts.

Here's one example from researchers at the University of Idaho:

Preliminary research had indicated that beta-carotene, vitamins C and E and selenium were key dietary nutrients in the protection against several cancers. Later research showed that carotenoids (not beta-carotene specifically) and vitamin C may provide protection. However, when these conclusions were tested by supplementing the diet with these specific nutrients, provided singly or in combination, the results were not clear.

To single out the nutrient(s) most researched, or most easily measured, or best known as an antioxidant of choice against cancer is a mistake. The present evidence makes it appropriate to conclude that foods rich in antioxidants and bioactive compounds, mainly fruits and vegetables, protect against cancer. The effect of the whole food is more powerful than the effect of a specific dietary nutrient.

Eating foods that are as close to their whole state as possible provides the greatest potential for capturing this synergistic effect.

Organic Food: Better for Us and the Planet

While the data on the nutritional content of organic versus conventional produce is not completely in, a number of important studies indicate that organic produce packs a greater nutritional punch than conventional produce given similar growing conditions, freshness and storage.

A four-year study funded by the European Union compared a number of crops grown side by side on a 725 acre site near Newcastle University in England. The study results showed 20 to 40 percent higher levels of antioxidants in organic versus conventional wheat, tomatoes, potatoes, cabbage and lettuce. Various studies of conventional versus organic produce at the University of California at Davis have shown higher levels of antioxidants, polyphenols, Vitamin C and some minerals in everything from sun-dried tomatoes to kiwis.

"When the health of one link of the food chain is disturbed, it can affect all the creatures in it. When the soil is sick or in some way deficient, so will be the grasses that grow in that soil and the cattle that eat the grasses and the people who drink the milk."

– Michael Pollan, "Unhappy Meals"

Even if the research is as yet inconclusive, these results make sense. Organic growers focus on maintaining soil health. Healthier soil rich in nutrients seems likely to translate into more nutrient-dense plants. Plants grown in healthy soils have the capacity to develop compounds that fight predators and disease. These compounds are passed on to us when we eat the vegetables, and help us in similar ways to resist infection and illness.

Beyond that, pesticide and herbicide use has enormous consequences for the health of the interconnected web of life that makes up our planet. If the planet isn't healthy, our long-term health clearly suffers as well. Pesticides have been linked to diseases from cancer to Parkinson's. For the sake of all of us, we encourage you to purchase organic foods whenever possible.

Making the change to a healthier diet starts with these three simple ideas. Eat a diet made up primarily of whole foods. Have at least ⅔ of your plate be plant foods such as vegetables, grains, beans and fruit. Choose organic foods whenever possible. If you keep these concepts in mind, and slowly but surely move your diet in these directions, you'll be on your way to better health.

apple

The American Institute of Cancer Research's Ten Recommendations

In November 2007, the World Cancer Research Fund (WCRF) and the American Institute of Cancer Research (AICR) published their *Second Expert Report on Food, Nutrition, Physical Activity and the Prevention of Cancer*. The study includes the following eight recommendations:

1. Be as lean as possible without becoming underweight.

2. Be physically active for at least 30 minutes every day.

3. Avoid sugary drinks. Limit consumption of energy-dense foods (particularly processed foods high in added sugar, or low in fiber, or high in fat).

4. Eat more of a variety of vegetables, fruits, whole grains and legumes such as beans.

5. Limit consumption of red meats (such as beef, pork and lamb) and avoid processed meats.

6. If consumed at all, limit alcoholic drinks to 2 for men and 1 for women a day.

7. Limit consumption of salty foods and foods processed with salt (sodium).

8. Don't use supplements to protect against cancer.

And these two recommendations for special populations:

9. It is best for mothers to breastfeed exclusively for up to 6 months and then add other liquids and foods.

10. After treatment, cancer survivors should follow the recommendations for cancer prevention.

Simple and Satisfying: How To Nourish Yourself During Treatment with Almost No Cooking

Supporting our body through what we eat is relatively simple when we are well but becomes a bigger and more important challenge when we are dealing with a critical illness. Illness changes how our energy is used, effects our appetite and ability to eat, and adds nutritional demands. When we are ill and healing from a serious illness, every bite counts.

During a serious illness, the loss of vital energy may be one of the most difficult obstacles we face. Our store of energy is what allows us to do the physical, emotional and mental activities we aspire to during our waking day. Pain associated with illness can further deplete our reserves as the body seeks to repair itself.

How can you feed yourself well during those times – days, weeks or perhaps longer – when you have absolutely no energy? If you have enough money and a good quality grocery store in your neighborhood, you may be able to purchase a healthy array of ready-to-eat prepared foods. If you are blessed with friends and family nearby, they may be able to help by cooking some or all of your meals for you.

If you are like many of our clients, however, you have no extra money and very little support. In this section, we want to give you some suggestions for how to get the most nourishment with the least amount of work if you are ill and fending for yourself.

Here's a simple plan to use as a guideline.

Basic Weekly Plan

1. **Make a batch of Immune and/or Chicken Bone Broth.** Broth requires almost no chopping – most vegetables can be simply cut in two or three pieces and covered with water. It cooks unattended for 2 to 4 hours and you have a high-quality source of nutrition that you can sip either warm or cold.

    Immune Broth (page 186) is a potassium rich vegetable broth that is alkalinizing for the body. Chicken Bone Broth (page 187) includes organic bones that are cooked with vinegar or lemon juice for 12 to 24 hours to help draw out the marrow, creating a broth that is protein-rich.

2. **Cook 2 cups of a grain of your choice.** Soak the grain overnight, and then cook the grain using Immune Broth or Chicken Bone Broth instead of water (perhaps from your freezer if you've been able to make some at an earlier time), or purchased vegetable or

chicken broth. Add a piece of kombu (see Sea Vegetables, page 34) to add minerals and make the grain even easier to digest.

This will give you about 5 cups of a whole grain enhanced with the nutrients from the broth and sea vegetable. If you use a chicken broth, you'll have some added protein. Making the grain will take five minutes or less to start and then will cook virtually unattended for 15 to 40 minutes (depending on the grain you choose). A rice cooker with a timer will allow you to walk away and be assured that your grain will not burn.

3. **Make a batch of muesli.** Pour an equal amount of plain whole milk, non-dairy milk, kefir, or yogurt over some regular rolled oats and put it in the refrigerator. Let it sit overnight and then eat small amounts at a time with nuts, seeds and/or a bit of fruit. Adding a mashed banana or a bit of unsweetened applesauce will sweeten the muesli without sugar. (See recipe on page 60.)

4. **Use your blender to make smoothies.** Start with a dairy or non-dairy milk, kefir or coconut milk. Add whey or rice powder for added protein, a green powder, lecithin (which helps improve liver and gallbladder function and supports the health of cells) and fruit. See pages 67 and 68 for a few basic smoothie recipes.

5. **Add a few vegetables** – here's a list of cooked and raw vegetables that require almost no preparation:

   - Baked sweet potatoes, yams or regular potatoes
   - Baked acorn, butternut or other winter squash
   - Raw carrots, celery, cherry tomatoes, tiny asparagus spears, red, yellow or orange sweet peppers, cucumbers, romaine lettuce, spinach, arugula.

6. **If you are eating chicken or fish,** bake a small piece in the oven just until it is cooked through. Cool slightly, refrigerate and eat small amounts daily either warm or cold.

If you have a bit more energy, you might include the following:

7. **Make a miso soup** using Immune Broth, Chicken Bone Broth or a purchased broth as a base. The simplest recipe is to heat the broth, take it off the heat and stir in miso to taste. You can also add some washed and sliced greens, or about any other vegetable you have on hand. Cook the vegetables in the broth until they are tender, take it off the heat and stir in miso to taste. Including a bit of sea vegetable such as arame, wakame or crumbled nori, will add even more nutrition.

8. **Steam or roast 3 to 5 cups of vegetables** and put them in smaller containers to heat as you like. (See Basic Vegetable Cooking on page 50.)

9. **Make a soup or stew in a crockpot.** Here are three suggestions for simplicity, balanced nutrition and digestibility:

Tip

Add nut butter, tahini or (purchased) guacamole or hummus to the raw or cooked vegetables along with a few whole grain crackers or bread and you have a nourishing snack with good quality protein, fats and carbohydrates in every bite.

"We have forgotten what really nourishes us, and when we fail to connect with things, life becomes empty and deadening. To see food merely as fuel or stuff is impoverishing. Enlightenment or realization in Zen is sometimes referred to as 'attaining intimacy'. It is to actually touch and know through and through, to digest and grow. We cannot be more intimate than we are with food; it becomes us."

– **Ed Brown,**
Tomato Blessings and Radish Teachings

- Fennel Carrot Congee (page 188)
- Kitchadi Plus (page 126)
- Split Mung Dahl (page112)

Building your physical energy takes time. Getting into a few new daily habits can help. Remember:

- When your appetite is low, take small meals and focus on foods that pack a nutritional punch.
- Eat the colors of the rainbow for the maximum nutritional benefit.
- Drink often. Include broths and teas that nourish the body with minerals and helpful herbs along with plenty of pure water.
- Add condiments to your meals such as soaked nuts and seeds, nutritional yeast, goji berries and sea vegetables.

butternut squash

Understanding Sweeteners

Humans are born with the desire for sweet flavors. Mother's milk is sweet and it is the natural sugars in the milk that support the growth and development of the young child. Sweetness comes in many forms, however, and some are significantly better for our bodies than others. How we eat sweet foods also makes a difference in how we process them and hence their impact on our health.

The most important recommendation is to eat whole rather than refined foods. Whole grains, legumes, fruits and vegetables are healthy carbohydrates that provide a balance of whole sugars, fiber and, in some cases, protein. The complex nature of these foods means that we can digest them without a rapid rise in blood sugar.

While most people don't think of these foods as sweet, chewing them thoroughly will release their natural sugars. Many people discover that as they eat more whole foods, they begin to lose their desire for refined sweet treats.

Processed sugars like high fructose corn syrup and refined white sugar create a strain on the liver. The body cannot function correctly with excess sugar in the blood stream. The liver produces insulin to store the sugar in the body's tissues. Eating sugar frequently leads to an overload on the liver and an acidifying reaction in the blood. Many researchers now believe that a diet high in sugar leads to an inflammatory response in the body and an aggravation of many disease processes.

All Sugars Are Not Created Equally: The Glycemic Index vs. The Glycemic Load

Processed sugars are simple molecules that can flood the system with sugars. The body, needing to respond, creates high levels of insulin to capture the sugars and store them in the tissues. The *Harvard Women's Health Watch* reports:

> ...Not all carbohydrates act the same. Some are quickly broken down in the intestine, causing the blood sugar level to rise rapidly. Such carbohydrates have a high glycemic index (GI). Because rapidly rising blood sugar levels have various adverse effects, we advised eating plenty of fruits and non-starchy vegetables and few high-GI carbohydrates, such as refined grains and starches. We also endorse a food pyramid where fruits and non-starchy vegetables, not refined grains, occupy the bottom tier. The purpose of this advice is to reduce overall glycemic load (GL). –"Glycemic Load, Diet and Health"

About Honey

Honey is not recommended for children under one year of age due to the risk of infant botulism. For everyone else, using raw unheated honey is best as heating honey destroys the healthy enzymes, vitamins, and amino acids that it contains. If a recipe calls for honey and is going to involve heat, substitute brown rice syrup, maple syrup or turbinado sugar.

"The supermarket crammed with its thousands of brightly colored packaged offerings is a mirage: if you could wave a wand and break everything down into its constituent ingredients, a pool of high-fructose corn syrup would fill half the store. Real food really does taste better."

– Bill McKibben,
Deep Economy

The glycemic load (GL) is a relatively new way to measure the impact of carbohydrate consumption that takes the glycemic index (GI) into account, but gives a fuller picture than does the GI alone. A GI value tells you only how rapidly a particular carbohydrate turns into sugar. It doesn't account for how much of that carbohydrate is in a serving of a particular food. You need to know both facts to understand a food's effect on blood sugar. That is where the GL comes in.

A carrot, for example, has a GI of 47 – quite high – yet the GL is only 2. The reason for the difference is that your body's glycemic response is dependent on both the type AND the amount of carbohydrate you consume. That carrot includes a lot of fiber. The "net carbohydrates" after the fiber is accounted for is quite low, hence the low GL.

The GL is also affected by the other foods you eat with that carrot. Sautéing the carrot in a bit of olive oil or eating it with a small amount of chicken will reduce the GL even further because the fat and protein slow the release of the sugars even more.

If a food has a low GI it will always have a low GL. But foods that have an intermediate or high GI may surprise you – their GL can range from very low to very high, and you can influence this by how you prepare the food and what you eat with it.

Making Healthy Choices

Excess blood sugar levels are implicated in a wide range of disease processes including diabetes, heart disease and cancer. While everyone benefits from reducing the amount of processed sugars and simple carbohydrates in their diets, for those who are ill this may be critical.

If you want to include some sweet treats in your diet, here are our recommendations:

1. **Eliminate all refined sugars from your diet including white and brown sugar, fructose, and all forms of corn syrup.** Be aware that corn syrup is lurking in many processed foods. If you purchase any prepared/processed foods, please read the labels carefully.

2. **Stick with whole fruits.** Whole fruits include fiber which slows the release of sugars into the blood. Fruits also include a wide range of vitamins and minerals. Avoid tropical fruits like bananas and mangoes that are higher in sugar. Berries are safest.

3. **Experiment with stevia.** Stevia is an herb that has been used as a sweetener by the Guarani Indians of Paraguay for hundreds of years. The leaves of the stevia plant can be 30 times sweeter than sugar yet the body does not metabolize

Tip

For people with cancer, the greatest issue with sugars is that cancer cells have extra insulin receptors; they love sugar and grow quickly in its presence. Our recommendation is that people with cancer avoid all refined sugars, limit their sugar intake dramatically, and choose whole unprocessed sugars such as those listed below.

the glycosides from the stevia leaf so there is no impact on blood glucose levels.

4. Use sweeteners that are minimally processed and made from whole foods in very small quantities. If you are going to use a refined sweetener, choose barley malt, brown rice syrup, Barbados molasses, sorghum molasses, maple syrup, honey, date sugar, or unrefined cane juice. These sweeteners are less processed than other forms of sugar and include minerals, enzymes, vitamins and fiber. Because they are somewhat more complex, they are processed more slowly and hence keep insulin levels more stable.

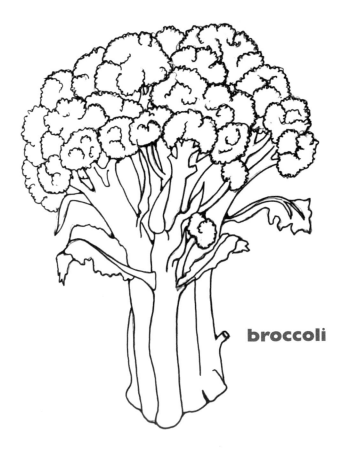

broccoli

Demystifying pH

Everything that we eat or drink, when digested, can be looked at in terms of pH, a measure of the acidity or alkalinity of a given substance. The body's blood pH needs to be slightly basic with an optimal pH value of 7.36. This is tightly regulated in a process called acid-base homeostasis. What does this have to do with health?

Eating a diet high in foods that are acid-forming puts stress on the body and acid blood conditions are believed to be one cause of the chronic inflammation that is linked to a wide range of diseases. When the body becomes acidic it seeks out alkalizing minerals such as potassium, calcium, and magnesium to buffer the system. Without enough minerals in the system to buffer a consistent condition of acidity, the nerves and bones will eventually give up their minerals. If the body stays in an acidic state, nutritional deficiencies, disease, inflammation, infection, and osteoporosis may take hold. What can you do to create the optimal alkaline environment?

While the body must maintain a blood pH of 7.36, the good news is that you don't need to carry an Acid-Alkaline Chart around to make informed choices about what to eat and what to avoid. Removing sugar and refined foods from your diet and increasing the amount of plant based whole foods will automatically support a healthy acid-alkaline balance in your body.

Avoid the most acidic foods – white sugar, processed/refined foods such as white flour, pastries, fried foods, cereals and alcohol.

Increase alkaline foods – vegetables, fruits, sprouts, *presoaked* beans and grains, and super-alkaline foods such as umeboshi plums, sea vegetables and miso.

Fats Dos and Don'ts

Fats are essential to maintaining good health. Every cell in our body is surrounded by a layer of fat. When that fat layer is healthy and intact, we can utilize nutrients more effectively and cell communication is more efficient. Fats are the carriers of the fat-soluble vitamins, Vitamin A, D, E, and K. They support the health of our bones, eyes, hair, weight management, nervous system, blood, immune system, and brain function. In fact over 65 percent of the brain is composed of fats! The hormones and hormone-like substances that are created from fats regulate many body systems including the endocrine system.

Our body's first choice of energy to burn is fats as they offer more calories per gram than protein or carbohydrates. Fats satiate our appetites and help us to moderate the digestion of sugars. How do we choose fats that are healthy and which fats do we need to avoid?

Most processed and fast foods are produced with fats that have been highly processed, sometimes using chemicals and often heated to a point where they are denatured. When fats used as cooking oils – like safflower oil or other vegetable oils – are processed with heat they become oxidized. This removes the vitamin E and changes the composition of the fat to a form that our cells do not recognize. One of the most important steps you can take in improving your health is to avoid processed and fast foods, and refined or heat-processed oils.

> *Many nutrition experts believe that before we relied so heavily on processed foods, humans consumed omega-3 and omega-6 fatty acids in roughly equal amounts. But to our great detriment, most North Americans and Europeans now get far too much of the omega-6s and not enough of the omega-3s.* [The ratio now may be as high as 25:1 rather than 1:1.eds.]

> *This dietary imbalance may explain the rise of such diseases as asthma, coronary heart disease, many forms of cancer, autoimmunity and neurodegenerative diseases, all of which are believed to stem from inflammation in the body. The imbalance between omega-3 and omega-6 fatty acids may also contribute to obesity, depression, dyslexia, hyperactivity and even a tendency toward violence.*

> *. . . you can cut down on omega-6 levels by reducing consumption of processed and fast foods and polyunsaturated vegetable oils (corn, sunflower, safflower, soy, and cottonseed, for example). At home, use extra virgin olive oil for cooking and in salad dressings. Eat more oily fish or take fish oil supplements, walnuts, flax seeds, and omega-3 fortified eggs.*

> – Dr. Andrew Weil

Fats to Avoid

- Hydrogenated fats, trans-fats, and interesterified fats (the newest manufactured fat that is modified to be more stable) found in processed foods like frozen waffles, cereals, baked goods, donuts, pastries, crackers, salad dressings, margarine, shortening, mayonnaise, and fried foods.
- Fried foods from most restaurants and all foods fried at high temperatures. Sautéing foods at a medium heat with coconut oil, ghee or olive oil is fine.
- Most polyunsaturated fats, especially refined vegetable oils such as canola oil, sunflower oil, safflower oil, peanut oil and corn oil.
- *Excessive* consumption of saturated fats such as butter, heavy cream, lard and animal fats.

Fats to Include

Include these three types of healthy fats in your daily diet:

- Monounsaturated fats such as cold-pressed olive oil or sesame oil, almonds and avocados.
- Polyunsaturated fats (omega 3 and 6's) from fresh cold-water fish, fish oils, flax or chia seeds, and olive oil. These fats are the most unstable and are damaged by heating or processing. Be sure to choose cold-pressed oil. Refrigerate nuts and seeds, and then eat them raw or freshly ground. The exception is chia seeds which are very stable and do not need to be refrigerated.
- A *small amount* of high quality saturated fats including organic butter and cream, organic whole milk products, organic cheese, coconut oil, and clarified butter or ghee.

The average person requires about 30% of their diet to be from healthy fats. To meet this goal, include some of these foods in your diet each day:

- Nuts such as almonds, walnuts, Brazil nuts, pecans and cashews
- Seeds including sunflower, sesame, pumpkin, flax, chia and hemp
- Avocados
- Organic whole, and if possible raw, dairy: butter, milk, yogurt, kefir andcheese
- Organic eggs

About Interesterified fat

Interesterified fat refers to a type of oil where the fatty acids have been moved from one triglyceride molecule to another. This is generally done in order to modify the melting point, slow rancidification and create an oil more suitable for deep frying or making margarine with good taste and a low content of saturated fatty acids.

- Sustainably caught cold water fish. Good choices that are low in mercury and high in omega 3 oils include sardines, wild caught Alaskan salmon and pollock, and wild caught herring and trout from Lake Superior
- Organic coconut products: coconut milk, oil, meat and butter
- Oils: cold-pressed organic olive oil, sesame oil, coconut oil, ghee, evening primrose oil and borage oil

What Kind of Fat for What Use?

- Oils like borage, flax, and evening primrose are best when used for salad dressings, but should not be heated.
- Olive oil is also most nourishing when unheated. If used for cooking, keep the heat low to medium. Do not let the oil reach the smoking point as this indicates that the oil is burning, changing the molecular structure and releasing free radicals which have been positively linked to cancer and other disease processes.
- Sesame oil is an excellent choice for cooking at medium heats. It has a lovely fragrance and a nutty flavor and also makes delicious salad dressings and marinades.
- For cooking at high heat, choose either coconut oil or ghee, a clarified butter which has a light, lovely taste. Neither of these oils needs to be refrigerated (unless the temperature is very warm) as they stay solid at room temperature and are very stable fats. Use them for frying, sautéing and baking, but note that coconut oil will add a coconut flavor to your dish.

Remember that fats need to be cared for so they don't go rancid. Store nuts, seeds and liquid oils in glass containers in the refrigerator or freezer.

Your body needs fats for energy and to maintain health. Replacing processed and trans-fats with the fats found in organic whole foods such as coconut, avocado and nuts is an important step in building a foundation of health.

The Secrets of Mushrooms

Mushrooms have been treasured as remedies for disease and as natural health supplements for thousands of years. In many Asian countries, supplementation with mushrooms is considered standard practice for patients undergoing chemotherapy and radiation. An increasing number of Western studies are supporting these claims for the benefits of mushrooms.

A few of the most potent – and most studied – varieties of mushrooms include reishi, cordyceps, maitake and shiitake. Most mushroom varieties are considered to be adaptogens – substances that help the body adapt to stress, support normal metabolic functions, and help restore balance. When the Chinese Olympic athletes were accused of using drugs to enhance their performance, it was actually cordyceps mushrooms that were responsible for their incredible stamina.

A growing body of research is supporting the use of mushrooms in both cancer prevention and in reducing the side effects of traditional cancer treatments. The combination of active ingredients in mushrooms seems to maximize the body's immune response which is vital to recognizing and eliminating tumor cells. A 2005 study by Cancer Research UK noted, "These compounds have been shown to be safe when taken over long periods of treatment and significantly, these compounds appear to reduce the adverse effects of radiation and chemotherapy."

In general, mushrooms work to facilitate the body's movement towards health. If you are not allergic to them and enjoy their flavor and texture, we suggest that you include two or three servings of a variety of mushrooms in your weekly menus.

Let's take a closer look at four different varieties of mushrooms.

Reishi is an immune enhancer which activates macrophages and interleukin production, natural killer T cells and tumor necrosis factors, and has anti-tumor, anti-viral, anti-inflammatory, antioxidant, cholesterol-reducing, and anti-fatiguing properties. It can protect the liver and help with detoxification. As an adaptogen, reishi supports all the major systems of the body when and where it is needed.

Reishi mushrooms are extremely woody and hence are inedible. Dried, sliced mushrooms are best simmered in stocks to release their nutritional value. Reishi is also available in supplement form.

About Reishi Mushrooms

Please note that reishi mushrooms should not be used for one or two days following treatment. Although research indicates that reishi may be effective in minimizing the side effects of chemotherapy and radiation, it may also interfere with these treatments.

Maitake are good sources of vitamins B_2, C, D and niacin, magnesium, potassium, amino acids, fiber and a polysaccharide, beta 1.6-glucan, that stimulates the immune system and lowers blood pressure. Maitake is known for its anti-tumor properties, especially against prostate, breast and colorectal cancer as well as lung cancer. It has been shown to lower or moderate glucose levels in the blood, and may help reduce bronchial infection. Maitake can be taken with chemotherapy and radiation and may help to both enhance the effectiveness of the treatments and reduce their side effects.

Maitake, also called "hen of the woods," can be sautéed and used in cooking. Florence Fabricant, the food editor of the *NY Times* says maitakes are "quite meaty, with a delicately nutty flavor." Maitake is also available in supplement form.

Shiitake mushrooms enhance the immune response of the natural killer T cells and interferon. Shiitake may act as an anti-viral agent, oxygenate the blood, and tone the liver. It may also reduce cholesterol levels. The cell wall of the shiitake mushroom contains a sugar known as lentinan. This protein-free polysaccharide has been shown to stimulate macrophages and help activate the lymphocytes and other immune cells.

Shiitakes are available fresh or dried in most grocery stores and Asian markets and can be used in any recipe calling for sliced, sautéed mushrooms. Sautéing a mixture of shiitake and white or cremini mushrooms together will reduce the amount of oil needed. Add sliced, sautéed shiitakes to miso soup, make Mushroom Barley Soup with a mixture of shiitake and other mushrooms, or add sliced shiitakes to stir-fries.

Cordyceps have immune enhancing properties as well as polysaccharides that inhibit tumors. Cordyceps may have positive effects on the cardiovascular and nervous systems. Studies confirm that cordyceps enhance aerobic capacity, reduce damage to cells caused by free radicals, and normalize immune function. In human studies, cordyceps have been found to prevent immunosuppression and help restore normal macrophage and natural killer (NK) cell activity.

Cordyceps are available as a powdered extract.

shiitake

Nutrient Dense Sea Vegetables

In recent years, sea vegetables – formerly called seaweeds – have become favorites in the whole foods arena. If you aren't already familiar with sea vegetables, you might be asking, "Why would anyone want to eat sea vegetables?"

The main reason is that sea vegetables provide a broad range of minerals that are bioavailable – readily available – to our bodies. Sea vegetables are an excellent source of iodine and vitamin K, a very good source of the B vitamin folate and magnesium, and a good source of iron and calcium, and the B vitamins riboflavin and pantothenic acid. In addition, sea vegetables contain good amounts of lignans, chlorophyll, protein, and phytonutrients with cancer-protective properties.

Lignans have been shown to inhibit angiogenesis, or blood cell growth, the process through which fast-growing tumors not only gain extra nourishment, but send cancer cells out in the bloodstream to establish secondary tumors or metastases in other areas of the body. In addition, lignans have been credited with inhibiting estrogen synthesis in fat cells as effectively as some of the drugs used in cancer chemotherapy. In postmenopausal women, fat tissue is a primary site where estrogen is synthesized, and high levels of certain estrogen metabolites are considered a significant risk factor for breast cancer. Research is also showing a link between low iodine levels and breast cancer. Sea vegetables with the highest iodine contents include bladderwrack and nori.

Incorporating sea vegetables into your diet is easier than you might think. Here are our favorite suggestions:

1. Whenever you cook grains, beans or soup stock, add a large piece of kombu. The minerals from the kombu will enhance the nutrient content of the dish and will also help make the beans or grains more disgestible and less gas producing

2. Keep a container of kelp or dulse flakes on the dinner table and sprinkle them on food instead of table salt. Grind kelp or dulse with toasted sesame seeds and sea salt to make gomasio, a traditional Japanese seasoning that boosts a double nutritional benefit. (see recipe on page 191)

3. Experiment with arame, a mild tasting, tender sea vegetable that looks like thin brown noodles. Easily rehydrated, it can be added to rice dishes, vegetable stir fries, rice noodles, and many other dishes.

"If a diet contains mostly foods poor in nutritional quality, or if it lacks protective foods such as fruits and vegetables, latent tumors will be in an environment favorable to their growth, and thus risk turning into mature tumors. . . On the other hand, if the diet is rich in a good variety of protective foods and only contains a quite small percentage of 'dangerous' foods, the microtumors fail to grow and the risks of developing cancer are therefore much lower."

– Foods to Fight Cancer

Here's a brief overview of the major types of sea vegetables available in the United States:

Kombu adds a deep easy flavor without tasting like the sea. As a member of the kelp family it has many uses including supporting the kidneys and thyroid function, and helping to check candida, anemia and edema. Kombu can be added to grains, legumes and soup stocks, or brewed as a tea. After cooking, remove the kombu, chop it finely and add it back into your dish.

Hijiki is a strand-like sea vegetable similar to arame but with a stronger, saltier flavor. Hijiki adds calcium, iron and iodine as well as B_2 and niacin to our meals. Bones, nerves, hormones and blood sugar are supported by eating hijiki. Hijiki can be used interchangeably with arame but requires brief cooking.

Arame has many of the same healing qualities as hijiki but has a milder flavor and more tender quality, making it a favorite among novice sea vegetable eaters! Eating arame without rehydrating it adds crunch and a bit of salty flavor to salads, grains or trail mix.

Nori is familiar to many as the wrapping for sushi. Nori is 48 percent protein by dry weight, and contains high levels of vitamins A, B_1 and niacin. Nori's mild flavor makes it easy to eat. Nori sheets can be toasted over a flame or in the oven and eaten as a crunchy snack. For even more flavor, first brush the nori with a mixture of sesame oil and tamari. Add nori flakes to miso soup or a favorite grain dish to boost the nutritional value as well as support healthy digestion.

Dulse is rich in iodine and manganese, which helps promote enzyme activity. It also contains carotenoids that help support our immune system. Dulse's high iron content (compared to other sea vegetables) means that it should be avoided by cancer patients as iron is an oxidizer, leading to the release of free radicals. Found at the market as flakes or strips, dulse can be added to foods instead of salt.

Wakame has a calcium content that rivals milk and is easier to absorb! It counteracts growths and tumors. Wakame promotes hair growth and healthy skin, and supports the body's energy. Having a full-bodied flavor, it can be added to soups, stews, vegetable dishes, grains and stir fries, or used in place of kombu for cooking beans and grains.

Sprouts for Health

Why sprout when you can eat the whole radish, cook the lentil, munch on the pumpkin seeds, or boil the groats? There are four good reasons to sprout beginning with their enormous nutritional benefits.

1. **Nutrition Powerhouses:** Sprouted seeds, legumes, nuts and grains are in their nutritional prime. Studies show that sprouts – the germinating seed of a plant – produce 10 to 500 percent more vitamins, minerals, proteins and enzymes. Eating sprouts gives you the most nutrient-dense form of that particular plant. Sprouting also predigests the phytate-containing seed coat which our stomachs cannot readily breakdown, helping to make sprouts easy on delicate digestive systems. Sprouting also changes legumes into vegetables, reducing the gas and bloating that may occur when eating foods like lentils and garbanzo beans.

2. **Economical:** Sprouts provide high levels of nutrition at a low cost and in minimal space. Considering our economic times this is good news! Buying ¼ cup of seeds yields seven to ten times the volume of edible food stuff in a nutrient-dense form. All you need is a quart jar and a bit of counter space.

3. **Local and Fresh:** You've heard about the benefits of buying local. You get to support local merchants and farmers, take less energy to get the food home, and eat fresher food. Your kitchen is as local as you can get. The seeds may travel to your location, but then you get to decide when, where, which seeds, how much and how often they are sprouted. Even in the middle of winter you can create a fresh supply of sprouts.

4. **Verifiably Organic:** Organic becomes practical, economical and simple when it happens in your kitchen. Start with seeds bought from a reputable organic source, use filtered water or a reliable source of clean water, and you can create organic food right in your kitchen.

For instructions on how to sprout your own seeds, see How to Get Started with Sprouting on page 54.

It's not easy to eat well when you're going through surgery recovery, chemotherapy and radiation. Even though you clearly know what you should eat: organic, lots of vegetables, enough protein, whole grains. Standing at the stove is a stretch, chopping vegetables is a dream from the past, and shopping at the grocery store feels like climbing Mount Everest.

I'm feeling strong, and even back to work four months after completing treatment, to a large degree because of the Ceres Community Project. Not only because of the incredible food that sustained me, but because Ceres gave me so much more than food.

The deep healing intention and caring consciousness was there each time I opened the container and found beauty, balance and, I have to say it, love.

Moreover, this was a gift for me from strangers. Strangers who realize that it takes a lot of work to heal, and who, amazingly, truly care about me – a complete stranger. These weekly phenomenal acts of deep kindness (for that is what Ceres is about) helped me know that I was, and am, connected to a much larger and kinder world than the confines of my illness and treatment. That I was and am part of a deeply conscious and loving community of hearts.

The gratitude I feel about this is indescribable and life-changing. And I'm realizing that for me, gratitude is the biggest healer of all. And so I thank everyone at Ceres for making this incredible support available to me and to so many others.

~ Kathleen Kraemer

One Client's Story

Thursday
I'm tired. I feel crummy.
Still in my nightgown in the afternoon.
Laying on the sofa.
I remember... it's Thursday.
Day of the shopping bag Ceres angels.
This thought... makes me happy.

Saturday
Everything seems to hurt. Feel sick...
Can't remember what day it is...
just want to lie here in the dark room.
I should get up. Should eat. Don't feel like it.
Remember...the Ceres Angels bearing gifts.
Remember... that I hate to waste good food.

I open the fridge. Nifty plastic container says
"Chicken in Orange Ginger Sauce with
Rice and Vegetable Medley".
Hhhhmmmm. .. okay... well... sexy name!
I open the enticing box and see colors
that remind me of the garden I love.
I'll give it a try... just a bite, anyway,
just in case I can stand it.
Fork to mouth.
Oh!... taste buds surprise my brain.
Oh... wow! That was good!
Think I'll take another bite to be certain.
I sit down. Take another bite.
Eat the entire serving,
amazed that I find myself wishing there was more.
I'm clearly full..., but I'm drawn back to the fridge.
Hhmmm... "Mushroom Strudel with
Stuffed Artichokes".
I like the sound of that...
I look forward to the next time I
"should" eat... to the next opportunity
to be surprised, delighted, and deeply nourished.

Chapter 2 • Cooking Basics

Making Cooking Fun and Manageable

Creating nutritious meals for yourself doesn't need to feel like a chore, nor does it need to take a huge amount of your time.

Creative, Meditative, Fun and Nourishing

Preparing food is akin to painting with a pallet of flavors, colors, aromas, and textures. Thinking of your meals as your art will awaken your creativity and help make the entire process more satisfying. When you shop, let yourself be drawn to the colors and textures of the produce. When you cook, let your senses come alive to the sounds, the smells and the tastes. When you eat, let your whole being absorb the beauty and nourishment of your food.

Let go of thinking that there is a right way to cook and the entire process can become a time to relax, slow down and be present. Our lives are often full of busyness and we rush through our days packing in as many tasks as possible.

The good news is that you can't hurry food! The onions will take as long as they need to caramelize into a golden sweetness. The broccoli will be crisp tender when it's good and ready. Cooking can slow us down again to a more natural pace, allowing our bodies and our beings to settle and let go. Creating an hour a day to cook can be one of the best gifts you can give yourself. Not only do you end up with nourishing meals, but your spirit will be nourished as well.

In the kitchen, anything goes. If you've grown up cooking with recipes, this idea can be both liberating and a bit unnerving. In the pages that follow, we'll show you that with a few basic skills in your tool kit you can learn to trust your own instincts in the kitchen and cook to please your own body and sensibility from day to day.

Ultimately, our hope is that your entire relationship with food becomes a source of nourishment in your life – from consciously gathering produce in a local market or in your garden, to preparing it with love in your kitchen, and finally eating it with gratitude alone or surrounded by friends and family.

Keeping it Simple

Thinking about cooking can seem overwhelming if it isn't already part of your life. The tasks – planning, shopping, chopping, cooking and cleaning up – when taken together can feel daunting and you may be tempted to stop before you even start.

In this section, we help you break down the tasks into manageable steps that can happen at different times in your week or day.

1. Dream

Plan a simple menu for the week with some easy breakfast foods, two lunch items, two dinner ideas and several things you can snack on. For example, you might want to cook a grain with some dried fruit for breakfast and also make sure you have ingredients on hand for a breakfast smoothie. Lunch items might include a soup or stew plus a purchased hummus and two or three different steamed or roasted vegetables. For dinner, you might make a casserole that you can freeze half of for another week, two roasted chicken breasts or some tempeh treats, and a dish of sautéed greens.

2. Check your pantry and create a shopping list.

Keeping a pantry stocked with the basics will keep your weekly shopping simpler and give you more options on a day to day basis. (See Organic Shopping List in the appendix for ideas on what you might keep on hand in your pantry.) Once you've checked your pantry, make a shopping list for the week. Remember, shopping is a great job for a friend or family member who wants to help.

3. Organize a cooking day with a friend or family member.

Cooking with someone else makes the whole process both more fun and more manageable. You can have a friend help you cook for yourself or cook with someone else who also needs meals and share the results of your day.

Cook as many meals as you can. Remember, if you get through the cooking in one afternoon you won't have to cook the rest of the week.

Before you get started, read through the recipes you plan to make and figure out what will take the longest. Start with those tasks

> *"Enjoying your food is very important, because by enjoying something we connect to the world, to one another, to our inner being. When you enjoy your food you will be happy and well nourished by what you eat. Sometimes I also explain to people that by enjoying their food, they will naturally find themselves practicing meditation. They will be paying attention to what they are eating, noticing flavors and textures and nuances of taste, because to enjoy something you need to experience it... Entering into full enjoyment, they will be relaxing and opening their hearts to the food."*
>
> – Ed Brown,
> *Tomato Blessings and Radish Teachings*

first, along with things like cooking a pot of rice – which takes just a minute to start and then can happen unattended as you work on other things.

4. If you cannot cook with others, reserve your energy by breaking up the cooking tasks.

If you are cooking alone and your energy is at a low ebb, do your cooking in discrete chunks throughout the day or over several days. Here are some ideas:

- Most vegetables can be prepared ahead of time and then stored in the refrigerator until you are ready to cook. If you chop potatoes, store them in cold water to prevent browning. If you need onions for three different dishes, prepare the entire amount at once. Use a food processor for jobs like chopping onions, shredding carrots, and making pestos.

- Roast, steam or sauté vegetables in advance to either be used in other dishes or simply to have ready to eat. Vegetables can be stored for later use in glass containers, like the ones that Pyrex now makes with plastic lids.

- Make two quarts of broth in a slow cooker while you nap or overnight. Include the tops and peelings of the vegetables you have prepared along with some coarsely chopped whole vegetables. (See page 186 for our Immune Broth recipe.)

- The next day make one or two different grains for the week using your broth instead of water.

- Use your slow cooker again and make a soup using the rest of your broth. A recipe that makes six to eight cups will give you one cup of soup each day.

- Soak beans overnight, or sprout them (see page 54) to reduce their cooking time.

- Clean up as you go and know that if you are too tired, the dishes can wait!

5. Slow cook and freeze to save time and energy.

- Many stews, chilies and soups can be made without any attention on your part using a slow cooker. Put in the ingredients, turn it on low and head off to work or to bed. You'll return home or wake up to a lovely aroma.

• Freeze half of whatever you make. This allows you to have some soup and a few main dishes in the freezer – giving you more variety in the weeks to come as well as some options for those days when you just don't have the energy to cook.

6. Keep a few simple snacks on hand.

Keeping a variety of healthy snacks on hand can be a great help when you don't feel like a meal but know you need to eat.

• Cut up raw vegetables such as jicama, red bell peppers or carrots and store them in the fridge; steam cauliflower; roast acorn squash halves. Many stores carry washed, chopped vegetables that are ready to eat.

• Cut up fruit, dip it in some water with a bit of lemon juice to keep it from browning, and store it covered in the fridge.

• Make or purchase hummus, avocado dip and nut butters.

• Freeze a smoothie in plastic Popsicle containers for a nourishing and refreshing treat.

Remember, these are just suggestions. Do as much or as little as you have the energy for. Ask for help from friends or family members, or find a cooking buddy to help make the process more enjoyable. If you haven't cooked much, making this a regular part of your life will take time. Start simply and celebrate your accomplishments. Change takes time, but even small changes can reap big rewards physically and emotionally.

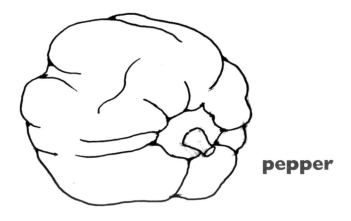

pepper

Kitchen Tools

Having the right tool for the job will make your cooking experience both more pleasant and more efficient. The best way to discover what you need is to start cooking. As you work in the kitchen, make a list of the things you wish you had. This way, you will slowly gather the tools that you'll actually use.

Here are a few suggestions of things we think are especially useful, or that we know you will need for the recipes that follow.

Knives & Knife Sharpeners

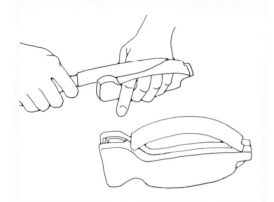

There is nothing as important as having a good quality, sharp knife. Believe it or not, at The Ceres Community Project we buy our knives from a local Asian grocery store. These cleaver style knives come in multiple sizes and offer blades that are straight or curved. They cost $3.99 each and, if sharpened regularly, will give you many years of service. The curved knives are especially useful for mincing herbs.

Experiment and find what works for you. Many chefs have a whole set of different knives for different jobs. If you are just starting to cook, we recommend getting a basic knife that you can use for most jobs, plus a knife for mincing herbs, and a paring knife for small jobs.

Invest in a good knife sharpener and sharpen your knife every time you begin cooking. There are many good table top knife sharpeners available that will sharpen your knife simply by drawing it through the middle. No special skills are needed and you can leave it sitting on your counter to remind you to sharpen your knives regularly.

Handy Utensils

Here are the utensils we use most often:
- Long- handled wooden spoon
- Rubber spatula, perhaps a few in different sizes
- Whisk – again, a few in different sizes may be useful
- Metal spatula
- Good quality peeler
- Microplane for zesting oranges, lemons and limes
  (this looks like a ruler and has small grating holes on it
  that allow you to zest the skin of citrus fruit without
  getting the white, bitter pith)

Spider

A spider has a long handle with a mesh "basket" on the end. You can find them at good culinary stores and Asian markets. A spider is a great tool to have on hand for blanching vegetables. It will allow you to scoop out whatever you are cooking so you can re-use the water for another vegetable.

Fine Mesh Strainer & Colander

If you plan to eat quinoa, you'll need a fine mesh strainer in order to rinse the tiny grains before soaking. Of course, there are many other uses for this tool! Add a larger colander for draining vegetables and pastas and you should be able to handle every rinsing and draining job in your kitchen.

Immersion Blender

This is one of the handiest tools as it allows you to blend soups and sauces easily while they are hot. You can leave whatever you are blending right in the bowl or pot, minimizing the number of dishes you will have to wash.

Spice Grinder

A good quality coffee or spice grinder is essential for finely grinding things like flax and sesame seeds.

Mini Food Processor/Food Processor

If you are cooking for one or two, a mini food processor is a great choice. You can easily chop small amounts of vegetables or nuts, make a pesto, or blend together a salad dressing. It doesn't take up much room and is quick and easy to clean.

If you like to make larger batches of things, or want to use the processor for grating and chopping vegetables, you'll want a regular size one. These are also wonderful for making hummus and other vegetable dips and spreads.

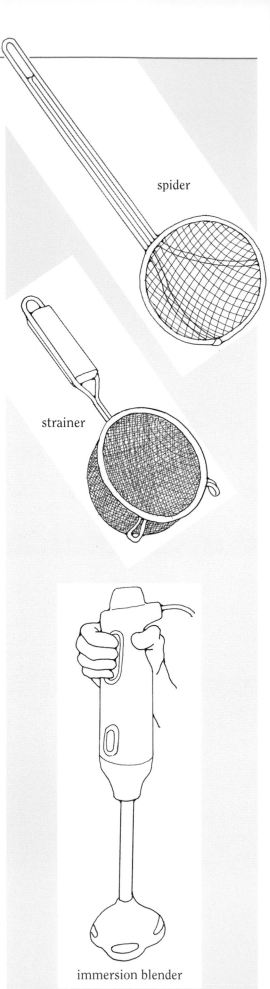

spider

strainer

immersion blender

Rice Cooker

These come in a variety of sizes and will let you cook almost any grain totally unattended. You can also add seasonings, chopped onions, minced garlic or ginger, coconut milk, etc. and create an instant pilaf. Try to avoid the Teflon coated cookers, as Teflon has been found to leach into the food.

Slow Cooker

This old stand-by is enormously helpful when you have limited time and energy. Put all your ingredients in the slow cooker, turn it on low and let it cook overnight or all day. You can make enough of a nourishing soup or stew to feed yourself for most of a week with just a few minutes of chopping and measuring.

Vita Mix

If you have the resources, we encourage you to invest in a Vita Mix. Nothing beats this all-in-one tool for juicing, smoothies, sauces, grinding nuts and making nut butters, and puréeing soups to a velvety texture.

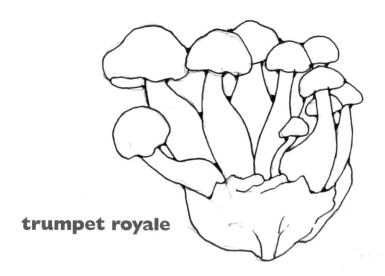

trumpet royale

Cooking Grains, Beans and Vegetables

Grains

Grains are an excellent source of fiber, protein, vitamins and minerals and have, for thousands of years, been the staple food for most cultures.

The health benefits of grains are greatly improved by a few simple steps: soaking grains before cooking, and cooking them with a sea vegetable such as kombu. Soaking grains for at least an hour, then discarding the soaking water, accomplishes two important things – it removes the phytic acid which inhibits the absorption of zinc, calcium, iron and other essential minerals, and it transforms the grains from acidic to alkaline-forming (see Demystifying pH on page 28). Cooking grains with kombu enhances the mineral content of the grains and further strengthens their alkaline effect.

According to Sally Fallon, author of *Nourishing Traditions,*

> *All grains contain phytic acid (an organic acid in which phosphorus is bound) in the outer layer of bran. Untreated phytic acid can combine with calcium, magnesium, copper, iron and especially zinc in the intestinal tract and block their absorption. . . Soaking allows enzymes, lactobacilli and other helpful organisms to break down and neutralize phytic acid.*

> *Soaking in warm water also neutralizes enzyme inhibitors, present in all seeds, and encourages the production of numerous beneficial enzymes. The action of these enzymes also increases the amounts of many vitamins, especially B vitamins.*

Grains vary in their protein, vitamin and mineral content. To get the best nutrition, include a good variety of grains in your diet.

Following are some basic guidelines to get you started. Experiment and discover what works best for you. Increasing the amount of liquid will give you a softer grain as will increasing the cooking time.

Consider investing in a small rice cooker and you'll make grain cooking that much simpler – you just add the soaked, rinsed grain, liquid and kombu or sea salt and turn it on. Please note that the ratios of grain to liquid that follow are based on soaking your grain for at least four hours and preferably overnight. If the grain is not soaked, you will need to increase the amount of liquid.

"You can learn many things about cooking, about ingredients, cutting, combinations, and procedures, but even more fundamentally you can learn to act on your own experience, outside of recipes, relying on your innate capacity to taste and sense and decide for yourself what you like."

– Ed Brown,
Tomato Blessings and Radish Teachings

Brown Rice, Whole Oats, Kamut & Wheat Berries

1 cup grain

1 ½ cups water or stock

1 – 2" piece of kombu or ¼ teaspoon sea salt

Rinse the grain and then place in a bowl and cover with water. Let soak for at least four hours or overnight. Drain, discarding the soaking water, and rinse well. Place the grain in a pot with the water and the kombu. Bring to a boil, reduce the heat to low and cover. Cook for 25 to 35 minutes, or until the water is absorbed and the grain is tender.

Experiment with the amount of water to get the consistency that you want. More water will yield a softer grain. If the grain is not tender and all of the water has been absorbed, add ¼ cup of water per cup of grain, cover and continue to cook for another 5 minutes, then re-check and repeat if necessary.

Barley & Wild Rice*

1 cup grain

4 cups water or stock

1 – 2" piece of kombu or ¼ teaspoon sea salt

Rinse wild rice or soaked barley and then place in a pot with the water and sea salt or kombu. Bring to a boil, cover and reduce the heat to low. Cook until the grain is tender, 25 to 30 minutes for barley and 35 to 40 minutes for wild rice. Drain excess water.

*Wild rice does not need to be soaked as it is actually a wild grass.

Quinoa

1 cup quinoa

¾ cup water or stock

1 – 2" piece of kombu or ¼ teaspoon sea salt

Rinse the quinoa well using a fine mesh strainer, then cover with water and soak for at least four hours or overnight. Drain, discarding the soaking water, rinse again, and then place the quinoa, ¾ cup water and kombu in a small pot. Bring to a boil, cover, reduce heat to low, and cook for about 10 minutes or until the water is absorbed and the quinoa is tender.

Millet

I cup millet

2 cups water or stock

I – 2" piece of kombu or ¼ teaspoon sea salt

Place the millet in a saucepan and toast over medium heat, stirring constantly, until the millet begins to have a nutty, toasted aroma. While the millet is toasting, bring two cups of water or stock to a simmer. Carefully add the hot water to the toasted millet along with the kombu or sea salt. Cover, reduce heat to low, and cook until the water is absorbed and the millet is tender, 20 to 25 minutes.

If you are making a salad with the millet, turn the grain out onto a cooking sheet and spread it out to cool. Once the millet is cool, use your fingers to separate the grains. It will resemble couscous.

To make millet porridge increase the water by 1 cup and cook slightly longer.

Bulgur Wheat & Couscous

I cup grain

2 cups water or stock

¼ teaspoon sea salt

Bring the water to a boil with the sea salt. Pour it over the grain, cover and set aside until the liquid is absorbed and the grain is tender, 15 to 20 minutes. Fluff with a fork.

Tip

Millet, bulgur and couscous contain low amounts of phytates and does not need to be soaked before cooking.

Beans and Peas

Legumes – or beans as we call them – are a wonderful source of protein, vitamins and minerals. Like grains, beans benefit greatly from pre-soaking. This not only greatly reduces cooking times, but also makes beans more alkaline by neutralizing phytic acid. Again, like grains, we recommend adding a bit of kombu to your cooking pot. Kombu helps make beans more digestible, reduces their gas-producing tendency, and adds valuable nutrients.

According to Dr. Steven Pratt, author of *Super Foods*,

> *The truth is that beans are a virtual wonder food. A delicious source of vitamin-rich, low-fat, inexpensive, versatile protein, beans deserve a place at the table for those reasons alone. But the full power of beans to lower cholesterol; combat heart disease; stabilize blood sugar; reduce obesity; relieve constipation, diverticular disease, hypertension, and type II diabetes; and lessen the risk for cancer make this ancient food an extraordinary and important addition to any diet.*

With the exception of lentils, we recommend pre-soaking all beans and peas. Rinse them well, then place in a pot and cover with at least four times as much water as beans. Soak for at least six hours and preferably overnight. Drain the beans, then place in a pot with water, covering by at least one inch. Add a generous piece of kombu and bring the beans to a boil. Reduce the heat to a simmer, partially cover, and cook until the beans are tender. Bean cooking times vary widely based on the freshness of the beans, altitude, and how long the beans were soaked.

1 cup of dry beans will yield about 2¼ to 3 cups of cooked beans. Beans freeze well so consider cooking a larger amount than you need and freezing the left-overs for future use.

Here are some rough guidelines:

Lentils: 18 – 20 minutes for use in salads, up to 35 minutes if you want them very soft

Split Peas: 45 – 60 minutes

Aduki & mung beans: 45 – 55 minutes

Most other beans will be tender in 30 minutes to 1 hour. To test beans, remove one from the pot and let it cool for a few minutes, then taste. The beans should be soft with no starchy taste.

Vegetables

There are an infinite number of ways to prepare vegetables, but if you understand the three techniques that follow, you'll have the basics for experimenting on your own.

Blanching and Steaming Vegetables

Blanching is a technique for cooking vegetables quickly in boiling water just until their color brightens and they no longer taste raw. You can also accomplish this same result by steaming vegetables in a steamer basket over boiling water. Blanching and steaming are great techniques for taking the raw edge off vegetables such as broccoli or even carrots, that you might want to eat cold or add to a vegetable salad. It's also the one method of vegetable preparation that involves no added oil.

Bring a pot of water to a boil with a bit of salt. The size of the pot and amount of salt depends on the quantity of vegetables you need to blanch. If you only have a few cups, use a two quart saucepan about ¾ full and add ¼ teaspoon of salt. When the water is boiling, add one kind of vegetable. As soon as its color brightens and it tastes just barely tender, use a spider or small wire mesh colander to remove the vegetables from the water. Rinse immediately under cold water to set the color and stop the cooking process. You can re-use your water to blanch any remaining vegetables.

Roasting

Roasting is one of the easiest and tastiest ways to cook vegetables. It concentrates their flavor by evaporating moisture and drawing the natural sugars to the surface so that the vegetables become slightly caramelized.

To roast vegetables, preheat your oven to 400° or 450° – a really hot oven is key! Chop your vegetables in the size that you like. The smaller the pieces, the quicker they will cook. We like about ¾ – 1½ inch pieces. If they are too small, they will dry out; if they are too large, they will take a long time to cook.

Toss the vegetables with a bit of sesame oil or ghee and salt and pepper, or add minced garlic and/or fresh or dried minced herbs. Place your oiled vegetables on a baking sheet in a single layer and roast them just until tender when pierced with a skewer or fork. Stir the vegetables once or twice during their cooking time to help them cook evenly.

"In a study that analyzed 252 cases of bladder cancer that developed in a population of 47,909 health professionals over a ten-year period, eating five or more weekly servings of cruciferous vegetables, particularly broccoli and cabbage, was associated with half the risk of developing cancer as compared to those individuals consuming one or fewer servings of these vegetables each week. Similarly, a study carried out on 5,000 Swedish women suggests that eating one or two daily servings of crucifers is linked to a 40 percent drop in the risk of developing breast cancer."

– Foods to Fight Cancer

Roast vegetables together that cook in about the same amount of time:

- Mushrooms, peppers, summer squash, green beans and onions will cook the quickest, in about 15 to 25 minutes, depending on their size and how done you like them.
- Butternut, sweet potatoes, potatoes, Brussels sprouts, cauliflower, turnips, carrots and eggplant will take 25 to 35 minutes.
- A few vegetables, like rutabagas, may take as long as 45 minutes to an hour.

Sautéing

Sautéing is a fancy word for frying. Here's the basic technique.

Put a bit of olive oil, coconut oil or ghee in a skillet or sauté pan. You want enough oil to thinly coat the bottom of the pan. Heat the pan over a medium heat. When the oil is hot, but not smoking, add your vegetables. Cook, stirring every few minutes, until the vegetables are tender. Once the vegetables are beginning to brown, adding a few tablespoons of water and covering the sauté pan can help finish the cooking process so that everything is tender. Keep an eye on things, however, as it is easy for the vegetables to become over-cooked.

Just as in blanching and roasting, the cooking times will vary depending on the size of the pieces and the density of the vegetable. Zucchini will cook faster than carrots, for example, and a thinly sliced piece of zucchini will cook faster than a thick slice. If you are cooking several types of vegetables, add the largest/most dense vegetables first. Let them cook for a few minutes, then add the rest of the vegetables and continue cooking until everything is tender.

If you are cooking a number of different vegetables and you aren't sure how long each will take, consider sautéing each one separately, removing it to a bowl while you cook the remaining vegetables. When all the vegetables have been cooked, return them all to the pan and warm for a few minutes before serving.

A Note about Nuts

Many of the recipes that follow call for nuts or seeds. Like grains and beans, nuts contain enzyme inhibitors that can restrict our ability to digest the nutrients they contain. Soaking nuts and seeds in water, then drying in a low oven or dehydrator, neutralizes the enzyme inhibitors and makes their nutrients more readily available.

Soak 2 cups nuts or seeds overnight in filtered water to cover. The next day, drain the nuts or seeds and spread them on a baking pan in a warm oven (not more than 150° to 200°) or place them in a dehydrator. Cook or dehydrate until they are completely dry and crisp. This will take 6 to 12 hours in your oven, 1 to 3 days in a dehydrator.

Fermenting Basics

Our ancestors have used the simple process of lacto-fermentation for thousands of years as a means of preserving foods without refrigeration or canning. Today we understand that beyond preserving foods, fermentation enhances their nutritional value. Eating small amounts of fermented foods on a daily basis helps to maintain healthy bacteria in the digestive tract. Healthy digestive bacteria are key to the digestion and absorption of the nutrients in our food.

> *The proliferation of lactobacilli in fermented vegetables enhances their digestibility and increases vitamin levels. These beneficial organisms produce numerous helpful enzymes as well as antibiotic and anticarcinogenic substances. Their main by-product, lactic acid, not only keeps vegetables and fruits in a state of perfect preservation but also promotes the growth of healthy flora throughout the intestine.* — Sally Fallon, *Nourishing Traditions*

Making your own sauerkraut is remarkably simple and extremely satisfying. Here are two easy recipes for fermented foods to get you started. If you are interested in exploring fermentation further, look at page 195 of the Resource Guide.

Tip

Make sure there is water over the cabbage or other vegetables as this is an anaerobic fermentation. Air will yield mold. If there is foam or some discoloration on the top layer of the sauerkraut just remove it as all the kraut under the water will be fine.

"Cooking is not merely a time-consuming means to an end, but is itself healing, meditation, and nourishment... We sell ourselves short when we concentrate on instant relief and instant gratification and do not see that work is how we make our love manifest."

– Ed Brown, *Tomato Blessings and Radish Teachings*

Basic Sauerkraut

5 pounds of cabbage, cored and shredded
   or chopped (save the outer leaves)

1½ tablespoons sea salt

4 – 6 tablespoons whey
   or an additional 1½ tablespoons sea salt

Optional Additions

Small handful of arame sea weed,
   soaked in hot water, then rinsed

½ – 1 tablespoon of finely minced or grated ginger

½ – 1 tablespoon of finely minced garlic

2 – 3 tablespoons fresh dill, minced

1 tablespoon caraway seeds or fennel seeds

1. Mix the cabbage with the salt and whey (if using). Add any optional ingredients. Pound the cabbage with a mallet or massage with your hands for about 10 minutes to release the juices.
2. Place the cabbage in a large glass jar or crock, pressing down firmly with your fist to pack the cabbage tightly. Liquid should cover the cabbage by at least ½ inch. Place the reserved outer leaves over the shredded cabbage.
3. Fill a smaller jar with water and place it inside the jar to weight the cabbage and keep it below the liquid.
4. Cover the jars with a towel and leave it at room temperature for at least 4 days and up to two weeks. Check the jar every few days to make sure the cabbage is still below the liquid.
5. Taste the sauerkraut on the 4th day to see if you like it. The sauerkraut is ready if it tastes good to you. When you like it, refrigerate it in a sealed jar, making sure there is water over the sauerkraut. It will keep for 6 months in your refrigerator.

Ginger Carrots

4 cups grated carrots

1 tablespoon freshly grated ginger

1 tablespoon sea salt

4 tablespoons whey or an additional 1 tablespoon sea salt

Follow the directions for Basic Sauerkraut.

How to Get Started with Sprouting

Creating your own sprouts at home is simple, satisfying and economical. For more information on sprouting and sprouting supplies, see pages 195 and 196 in the Resource Guide.

Basic Equipment

1. Glass mason jars
2. Straining lids for jars: A stainless steel mesh sprouting lid or tulle fabric or cheesecloth can be used with the Mason jar ring to secure it in place – or alternatively use a plastic sprouting lid.
3. Sprouting Bags: A nice option for legumes and grains.
4. An old dish drainer works well as a place to set the jars at a 45 degree angle. Rolling a towel under the jar may also work well.

Basic Directions

1. Soak suggested portion of seeds or legumes overnight in a bowl or covered quart mason jar.
2. Rinse the sprouts for 30 seconds with running water, drain and place them in a mason jar. Cover the jar with a straining lid, and place the jar at a 45 degree angle, lid side down, in a place with indirect light.
3. Rinse the sprouts for 30 seconds twice a day, in the morning and evening, draining well, then returning them to their upside down, 45 degree angle resting place. Do not let the seeds dry out. If it is hot, rinse more often.
4. Watch for the sprouts' tails to grow!
5. Remove the loose hulls by immersing the sprouts in a bowl of water; the hulls will rise to the top. Strain off the loose seed hulls.
6. When the sprouts are ready, rinse and store in glass containers or fabric bags in the refrigerator.

Other Tips

Clean sprouting equipment with food-grade hydrogen peroxide (3%) at ⅛ cup to a gallon of water or stronger if there is mold.

Rinsing sprouts with the above dilution of hydrogen peroxide before they are refrigerated helps keep molds away.

All stored sprouts need to be rinsed and drained daily.

> "In a sense, all discussion of local economies is about Fair Trade – about raising wheat and lettuce in a way that honors both farmer and soil; about growing timber in a way that allows loggers to work at a reasonable pace and in a living forest; about saving and producing energy in quantities that don't require military adventure or climactic upheaval. About giving up some measure of efficiency for other values."
>
> – Bill McKibben,
> *Deep Economy*

SPROUTING TIMES

Source: *Rainbow Green Live- Food Cuisine*, Dr. Cousens, http://supersprouts.com and *Sprouts, the Miracle Food*, Steve Meyerowitz.

Seed Type	Dry Measure	Soaking Time	Sprouting Time	Tips
Mung Beans	I cup	6-8 hours	4-5 days	2" tail- steam
Clover	3 Tbsp	5 hours	5 days	2" tail- hull- green
Radish	3 Tbsp	6 hours	5 days	2" tail- hull- green
Mustard	3 Tbsp	5 hours	5 days	1.5" tail
Broccoli	3 Tbsp	5 hours	5 days	1" tail- hull- green
Sesame Seeds	I cup	4 hours	2 days	1/8" tail
Wheat Berries	I cup	6 hours	5-7 days	4" tail
Spelt Berries	I cup	6 hours	5-7 days	4" tail
Rye Berries	I cup	6 hours	5-7 days	4" tail
Almonds	I cup	12 hours		dehydrate till crisp
Pecans	I cup	1-2 hours		dehydrate till crisp
Walnut	I cup	1-2 hours		dehydrate till crisp

A Final Word

Remember, great cooking begins with the freshest whole foods you can find. The best recipe in the world can't make up for mealy, flavorless tomatoes or bitter, tough greens. On the other hand, tender young greens out of the garden will be a delight raw or with just a quick sauté in olive oil and a sprinkling of salt and pepper.

Finally, we can't say this enough: Test and taste. Foods are infinitely variable and so are we! A carrot fresh out of the garden will vary in sweetness from a carrot that has been in the food system for a week or two. It might have a higher water content and cook more quickly as well. On top of that, what seems tender to me might not be tender enough for you. Your taste buds are unique – and may vary as well from week to week if you are going through treatment. When you cook, guidelines can be helpful but ultimately, cooking is about being present, paying attention, and learning to please yourself in this moment.

Chapter 3•Rethinking Breakfast

RECIPES

Coconut Banana Shake

Breaking Breakfast Out of the Box

As you've probably figured out by now, we don't believe that there are any rules about what to eat when. Just because it's called breakfast, doesn't mean that you have to automatically reach for a box of cereal or a carton of eggs. What we do believe is that you need to eat something – and hopefully that something will include a high-quality protein, a healthy fat, some fresh fruit or vegetables and a whole grain.

Here are some suggestions about food that makes a good start to your day. We hope these ideas will encourage your own creative thinking about that first meal. We've also included a few recipes for foods that fit into the traditional breakfast repertoire – but all of them include a nutrient-dense twist.

1. Leftovers make great breakfast food, including soups, stews and casseroles. Any hearty soup or stew that includes a grain and/or bean is a good choice. If your appetite is low, a bowl of miso soup with a few greens, a bit of brown rice and a few pieces of chicken could be a good choice. Leftover frittata, filo casserole or quiche also make great breakfast foods.

2. Any grain can be cooked into porridge by increasing the amount of liquid. If you soak the grain overnight you'll reduce the cooking time considerably. Add some diced dried or fresh fruit and cook until the grain is soft and you have something resembling a cooked cereal. Add a dash of vanilla and cinnamon and top with milk, a milk substitute, or yogurt. Try rice, millet, quinoa, amaranth (see recipe page 62), buckwheat or barley.

3. Eggs are simple, quick to cook and contain a good amount of high quality digestible protein. To increase the nutrient density of those eggs, try any of the following:
   • Poach an egg and have it with a sprouted whole grain English muffin and a side of fruit.
   • Sauté a few thinly sliced shiitakes and a couple thinly sliced leaves of kale or chard. When the vegetables are tender, add the eggs and scramble.
   • Warm a corn or flour tortilla, spread with vegan refried beans, top with scrambled eggs and slices of avocado. Add some grated cheese if you are eating dairy, or a spoonful of salsa.
   • Make French toast with an egg, some milk and a few slices of sprouted whole grain bread. Spread with applesauce and enjoy.

4. Especially when you just don't feel like eating, try a smoothie. Several recipes follow but essentially anything can work.

   • For a fruity smoothie, start with dairy or non-dairy milk, juice or water. Add one or two kinds of fruit, some whey or rice protein powder, a teaspoon or two of a high quality "green food", and some ground flax or chia seeds (see page 67 for information about these concentrated sources of nutrition). Blend until thick and creamy.

   • For a green smoothie, see our basic recipe on page 68.

5. Dessert for breakfast? Yes! The dessert recipes in this book have low or no added sugar, and many include a complex carbohydrate and/or a high-quality protein. If this is what sounds good, don't hold back! Dessert for breakfast might be:

   • Goji Stuffed Baked Apples topped with yogurt

   • Ginger Pear & Sweet Potato Upside Down Pie

   • Lily's Coconut Pudding with a side of fresh fruit and nuts

   • Rice Pudding

6. For the easiest breakfast possible, start with these ideas:

   • Sprouted whole grain bread or rice cakes spread with almond butter, cashew butter, or hummus and a piece of fruit.

   • Yogurt and fruit with some chopped nuts

   • Eggs and sprouted whole grain toast

   • Congee (page 188)

   • Immune Broth or Chicken Bone Broth (pages 186 and 187)

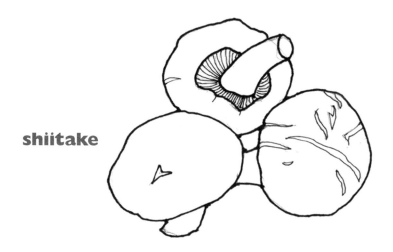

shiitake

Bircher Muesli

Prepared as a traditional Swiss snack or breakfast, Muesli was created by Dr. Maximilian Bircher, a late 19th century pioneer of nutritional research. He believed in eating healthy foods, exercising regularly, and taking time for a rest from daily life.

2 cups rolled oats

2 cups dairy or non-dairy milk or kefir

1 banana, mashed

1 apple, cored and diced or grated

Handful of almonds, roughly chopped, about ¼ cup

1. Put the dry oats in a large bowl and add your milk of choice. Stir to combine and then let the oats soak for at least 4 hours or overnight in the refrigerator.
2. The next morning, add the banana, apple and chopped almonds. Mix well and enjoy.

Serves 4

Tips

Soak the entire amount of oats and keep it in the refrigerator. Each morning, take out the amount you want to eat, add fruit and nuts, and enjoy.

For added nutrient density, sprinkle a tablespoon of ground flax seeds on your muesli right before eating.

Any seasonal fruit can be used, including pears, peaches, nectarines, strawberries, blueberries, raspberries or grapes.

apple

About Goji Berries

Goji berries or *Lycium Barbarum*, are a tart red berry used for centuries in Chinese medicine as a nutritive tonic for the liver, kidneys and blood. Modern research has demonstrated that goji berries are powerful antioxidants offering protection from free-radical oxygen molecules which can destroy cellular integrity and lead to inflammation, cellular degeneration and disease.

According to herbalists David Winston and Steven Maimes, goji berries "have been shown to enhance the effects of chemotherapy and radiation therapy while protecting cancer patients from leucopenia (decreased white blood cell counts)."

In addition to providing antioxidant protection, goji berries are a good source of vitamins A, B_1, B_3, and C, calcium, magnesium, potassium, chromium, copper, zinc, manganese, protein, fiber, and immune-building lyceum polysaccharides. Other constituents in goji berries have been shown to protect the cells from aging and inhibit cancer growth.

* Quinoa and barley flakes can be found in the hot cereal section of most natural foods grocery stores.

Complete Granola

While the list of ingredients looks long, the process of making granola is quite simple and requires just a few easy steps. You'll end up with a delicious granola that is much lower in added sugar than anything you can buy.

4 cups regular rolled oats

1 cup barley flakes*

½ cup quinoa flakes*

1 cup sesame seeds

1½ cup sunflower seeds

½ cup almonds, roasted and chopped

3 tablespoons coconut oil

2 tablespoons honey

2 tablespoons maple syrup

1 tablespoon vanilla extract

1 – 2 tablespoons ground cinnamon, or to taste

1 – 2 tablespoons ground cardamom, or to taste

½ cup unsweetened shredded coconut

¼ cup goji berries

¼ cup raisins

1. Preheat the oven to 300°.
2. In a large bowl, stir together the grains, seeds and chopped almonds.
3. In a small saucepan, heat the coconut oil over low heat. Whisk in the honey, maple syrup, vanilla and spices.
4. Add the coconut oil mixture to the dry ingredients and stir to coat the oatmeal mixture completely.
5. Place the granola on two cookie sheets, spreading to an even layer. Bake for 30 minutes, then stir and bake for another 30 minutes until the granola is golden and dried.
6. Cool, then stir in the coconut, goji berries and raisins. The granola will keep for several months stored in an airtight container.
7. Serve with milk, kefir or yogurt, and fruit.

Sweet Amaranth Breakfast Pudding

1 cup amaranth

3 cups water or half water and half dairy or non-dairy milk

¼ cup dried cherries

½ cup goji berries

6 dates, chopped

½ teaspoon ground cinnamon

½ teaspoon ground coriander

¼ teaspoon ground nutmeg

1 teaspoon vanilla extract

1 – 2 tablespoons honey or maple syrup (optional)

¼ cup almonds, toasted and chopped

Whole dairy milk or a non-dairy alternative

1. Combine the amaranth and water in a medium saucepan. Bring it to a boil, reduce the heat to low and add the dried fruit. Cover the pot and cook for about 20 minutes. The amaranth should be creamy.
2. Stir in the ground spices, vanilla, sweetener if you are using it, and the chopped almonds. Cook for an additional five minutes.
3. Stir in milk if desired and serve.

Serves 4

Tip

Is it breakfast or is it dessert? This is one of those recipes that can go either way.

This basic recipe can also be made with quinoa, millet or brown rice. Remember to soak the quinoa and brown rice overnight if you are using them.

About Amaranth Seeds

Amaranth seeds were a staple food of both the Aztec and the Mayan cultures. The beautiful red leaves of this annual herb are edible, and can be added to salads. Amaranth seeds are easily digested and protein rich, and include the essential amino acids methionine and lysine, which are not present in other grains. One cup of this gluten-free grain (uncooked) provides 26 grams of protein and 52% of an average adult's requirement for dietary fiber! So enjoy your amaranth pudding!

Adapted from *Recipes and Remedies for Rejuvenation* by Ed Baumann.

Variation

To make this with quinoa, soak ½ cup quinoa for at least four hours or overnight. Drain and rinse. Bring the quinoa and water to a boil, reduce the heat to low and cook for five to eight minutes. Add the milk and remaining ingredients, turn off the heat, cover and let sit for ten minutes.

"This weekly food delivery has been a real blessing. Being on chemotherapy has sometimes made it hard to even get from the bedroom to the kitchen, let alone prepare any meals. The Ceres food is gourmet quality and mostly organic...but so much more than that. I can feel that, so different from most restaurants, there is an important 'x' quality which I'm sure helps my healing – the food is made with love."

– Karen

Breakfast Couscous or Quinoa

1 cup water

1 cup whole dairy or non-dairy milk

½ cup couscous

¼ cup dried cranberries

¼ cup currants

¼ cup walnuts, toasted and chopped

½ teaspoon ground cinnamon

1 teaspoon vanilla extract

1. In a small saucepan, bring the water to a boil.
2. Stir in the milk and the remaining ingredients. Remove the saucepan from the heat, cover and let stand for ten minutes before eating.

Serves 2 – 3

Breakfast Berry Sauce

¼ cup goji berries

1 cup fresh or frozen blueberries

1 cup fresh or frozen raspberries

½ cup fresh or frozen blackberries

2 tablespoons honey or maple syrup

1 tablespoon ground cinnamon

1 tablespoon cornstarch or arrowroot

2 tablespoons water

1. Place all the ingredients except the cornstarch or arrowroot and water in a saucepan. Heat over medium heat, stirring frequently, until the mixture comes to a boil.
2. Whisk together the cornstarch or arrowroot and water until very smooth, then add the mixture to the berries, stirring constantly.
3. Continue to cook until the mixture is thick.
4. Serve warm over french toast, waffles or pancakes, or with oatmeal. Serve cold with yogurt or kefir and your favorite granola.

Serves 4 – 6

Applesauce Muffins

Do Ahead

- The dry ingredients can be mixed and stored, covered, a day ahead of time.

- The wet ingredients can be mixed and stored in the refrigerator a day ahead of time.

Tip

Make a batch of muffins and store them in a zip lock bag in your freezer.

Variation

Omit the dried fruit and add 1 banana, diced small, a peeled and diced apple, or ½ cup of blueberries.

1½ cup whole wheat pastry flour, or brown rice, oat, barley or quinoa flour

1½ teaspoons non-aluminum baking powder

¾ teaspoon cinnamon

½ teaspoon baking soda

½ teaspoon sea salt

Pinch ground cloves

1 cup applesauce

½ cup molasses

¼ cup vegetable oil

½ cup goji berries, raisins, dried cranberries or currants

¼ cup chopped walnuts, almonds or pecans

1. Preheat the oven to 350°. Grease and flour a 12 cup muffin tin.
2. Sift together the dry ingredients. In a separate bowl, whisk together the oil, molasses and applesauce.
3. Add the liquid ingredients to the dry and stir to mix well. Add the dried fruit and nuts and stir to combine evenly.
4. Divide the batter among the muffin tins.
5. Bake for 20 minutes or until a toothpick inserted in the center comes out with no wet batter.

Makes 12

apple

Flourless Almond Muffins

1½ cups raw almonds

¼ cup maple syrup

3 large eggs

1 teaspoon vanilla extract

¼ teaspoon sea salt

1. Preheat the oven to 375°. Grease a 12 cup muffin tin.
2. Grind the almonds in a food processor until they are finely ground like a flour, about three minutes. If the mixture gets sticky from the oil, use a spatula to scrape down the sides and loosen the mixture. Process for another minute.
3. Whisk together the maple syrup, eggs, vanilla and sea salt.
4. With the processor running, pour in the liquid ingredients and process until smooth.
5. If you are making any of the versions to the right, stir in the additional ingredients by hand, combining everything evenly.
6. Divide the batter among 12 muffin tins.
7. Bake for 20 to 25 minutes or until a toothpick inserted in the center comes out with no wet batter.

Makes 12

Tip

Make a batch of these wonderful treats and store them in the freezer.

Variations

- For Blueberry Lemon Muffins, add ½ to ¾ cup dried blueberries and 1 tablespoon of lemon zest.

- For Banana Coconut Muffins, add 1 banana, peeled and diced, and ¼ cup toasted unsweetened coconut.

- For Currant Spice Muffins, add ½ cup currants, ½ teaspoon ground cinnamon and ⅛ teaspoon each ground nutmeg and cloves.

This recipe is adapted from *One Bite at a Time* by Rebecca Katz.

Tip

Use fresh fruit and skip the ice cubes if you are getting chilled easily.

Variation

Freeze leftover smoothie in a popsicle mold for a refreshing treat.

About Flax Seeds

Known for being a good vegetarian source of Omega-3 fatty acids, flax seeds keep the heart and brain healthy. Flax seeds contain lignans which protect against breast cancer. To release the nutrients, flax seeds need to be ground. They go rancid easily, so store flax seeds in the refrigerator or freezer, and use ground flax seeds within a week or two

About Chia Seeds

Chia seeds are a rich source of stable Omega 3 fatty acids. Ground and added to breakfast porridge, grains or smoothies, chia seeds provide nutritional benefits similar to flax seeds. For constipation, try two tablespoons of ground chia seeds a day. Because chia seeds are more stable, they do not need to be refrigerated.

Coconut Banana Shake with Variations

½ – ¾ cup coconut milk

I ripe banana

½ cup fresh or frozen organic fruit: blueberries, strawberries, peaches, nectarines

I tablespoon ground flax or chia seeds

I scoop protein powder – whey, rice or hemp

2 – 3 ice cubes (especially if your fruit is not frozen) or a bit more water or coconut milk

1. Combine all the ingredients in a blender and blend until smooth.
2. Store leftovers in the blender in the refrigerator. Shake, whisk or blend again before serving.

Serves 1 – 2

banana

Spring Green Smoothie

I small handful spinach

I small handful spring bitter greens
   (dandelion, arugula, mache, kale)

½ cup fresh or frozen berries

I cup whole dairy or non-dairy milk, kefir or yogurt

I scoop protein powder – whey, rice or hemp

½ – 2 teaspoons spirulina or green powder

I tablespoon ground flax, chia or hemp seeds

I tablespoon honey or maple syrup (optional)

4 – 6 fresh fresh mint leaves (optional)

1. Put all the ingredients in a blender or Vita Mix and blend until smooth. Add more milk or a little water if you want a thinner consistency.

Serves 1 – 2

Variations

The keys to this green smoothie are the spinach, bitter greens, protein powder and green powder. Feel free to mix and match other ingredients as you see fit. Here are a few suggestions for things you might include:

- 1 banana or mango

- 1 teaspoon vanilla

- 6 soaked and dehydrated almonds or walnuts

- 1 teaspoon sesame tahini

- ½ – 1 teaspoon of a mushroom powder such as cordyceps, maitake, reishi or shiitake

- 1 handful of goji berries or acai berries or their juice

Having fresh food delivered to my home during my cancer treatment was an incredible gift. The Ceres Project offers a profound blessing to so many families who are struggling with the challenges of a cancer diagnosis. Not only did the weekly food deliveries help me to maintain a healthy diet, especially since I had so little energy for preparing food; I felt like I was being held in the nurturing embrace of the larger community. Cancer can be isolating, and the brief (and sometimes extended) visits with the people who delivered the food were as nourishing as the food, on an emotional and spiritual level. I am so grateful to all of the community members who make this project possible. Thank you!!!

Debora Hammond

Chapter 4•Salads for Every Meal

RECIPES

**Kale Salad
with Arame
& Sesame Seeds**

Asian Slaw with Sesame & Ginger

1 small head Napa, Savoy or regular green cabbage, very thinly sliced, about 4 cups

3 cups bok choy or tatsoi, very thinly sliced

1 carrot, peeled and grated

1 – 2 cups sugar snap or snow peas, strings removed, cut in two or three pieces on a diagonal

½ – 1 red, yellow or orange bell pepper, seeded and cut into thin strips

4 tablespoons toasted sesame oil

2 tablespoon umeboshi plum vinegar

1½ tablespoons tamari

1 tablespoon freshly grated ginger

2 tablespoons black sesame seeds, toasted

1. Bring a small pot of water to a boil. When the water is boiling, drop the sugar snap peas in and cook for 30 seconds. Drain and rinse under cold water, then drain well.
2. Whisk together the sesame oil, umeboshi plum vinegar, tamari and ginger. Taste and add more umeboshi vinegar if you want the flavor to be brighter.
3. In a large bowl, toss all the vegetables together, then add the dressing and the toasted sesame seeds and toss to coat.

Serves 6 – 8

Do Ahead

• Any or all of the vegetables can be prepared up to two days ahead of time.

• You can whisk together the dressing up to two days ahead of time.

Tips

• The amount and mixture of vegetables in this salad is very forgiving. You can use regular cabbage instead of Napa, substitute shredded kale or spinach for the tatsoi, omit the carrots or peppers – it's really up to you and what's on hand in your refrigerator or at the market.

• Use the slicing blade on your food processor to shred the cabbage and slice the peppers. Then switch to the shredding blade for the carrots.

• Feel free to add the sugar snap peas to the salad whole. You can also add them raw.

baby bok choy

Carrot & Goji Berry Salad

Do Ahead

- Everything can be prepared up to a day ahead of time.

- Consider preparing the vegetables for this salad and putting them in a large covered bowl in your fridge; prepare the goji berries, arame and toasted sesame seeds and store separately. Place the dressing ingredients in a small jar with a tight-fitting lid; shake well. When you are hungry, pull out as much as you feel like eating at the moment.

½ cup goji berries, soaked in water for ten minutes and drained

¼ cup black sesame seeds, soaked for ten minutes, then drained and toasted over low heat

¼ cup arame, covered with warm water for ten minutes and then drained well

½ head Romaine lettuce, leaves washed and spun dry

1 cup grated carrots

½ cup purple cabbage, thinly sliced

½ cup sprouted sunflower seeds (or substitute other sprouts)

¼ cup daikon radish, diced

¼ cup red, yellow or orange pepper, chopped

¼ cup fresh parsley or cilantro, chopped

¼ cup toasted sesame oil

1 tablespoon balsamic vinegar

1 teaspoon grated fresh ginger

Sea salt and pepper to taste

1. Whisk together the sesame oil, balsamic vinegar and fresh grated ginger.
2. In a large bowl, toss all the vegetables together with the dressing.
3. Add the arame, goji berries and toasted sesame seeds and toss just briefly to combine.

Serves 2 – 4

Cauliflower Salad with Cumin

*This lovely winter salad is a tasty way to add more cruciferous
vegetables to your diet.*

1 medium head cauliflower, broken into small florets

1 tablespoon olive oil

1 cup thinly sliced red onion

¾ teaspoon whole cumin seeds

¼ teaspoon sea salt

1 tablespoon apple cider vinegar

½ teaspoon minced garlic

4 tablespoons mayonnaise, sour cream or yogurt, or any
combination

½ cup diced cheddar cheese (optional)

¼ cup chopped fresh parsley

1. Steam the cauliflower just until it is tender, about five minutes,
   then drain and rinse under cold water to stop the cooking.
2. Warm the olive oil in a small skillet and then sauté the red
   onion and cumin seeds over medium heat until the onion is
   very soft. Don't hurry this process or you will burn the onion
   rather than melt it.
3. Whisk together the mayonnaise, cider vinegar, garlic and sea
   salt.
4. Combine all the ingredients in a large bowl, tossing to mix
   everything evenly. Taste and adjust the seasonings as needed.

Serves 4

Do Ahead

- The cauliflower and onion can be washed
  and chopped up to two days ahead of
  time.

- Mix your dressing up to two days ahead
  of time.

- Steam the cauliflower and sauté the
  onion and cumin seeds up to one day
  ahead of time.

Tip

- If you like, make this salad with broccoli,
  Brussels sprouts, or a combination of
  cruciferous vegetables – they all take
  well to this flavorful dressing. Just
  remember to steam each vegetable
  separately to insure that they are just
  tender.

- If you are avoiding dairy, use mayonnaise
  and omit the cheese.

Do Ahead

You can prepare any of the vegetables and herbs in the morning or the night before.

Tips

• This salad is lovely decorated with edible flowers such as borage or purple violets.

• To seed cucumbers, cut them in half lengthwise and then use a teaspoon to scrape out the seeds from each half.

• You can also try this with goat yogurt instead of the regular yogurt.

About Kefir

Kefir is a cultured, enzyme-rich food filled with friendly micro-organisms that help support healthy digestive bacteria. Made with cows milk or goat milk, kefir supplies complete protein, essential minerals, and valuable B vitamins. It can be purchased at most natural foods stores or easily made at home.

Cucumber Salad with Yogurt or Kefir

This recipe is nice in the summer months when cucumbers are abundant. The sweet and sour flavors are cooling and easy on the digestive system.

3 medium-sized cucumbers

2 scallions, trimmed and thinly sliced

1 tablespoon minced sweet red peppers or shredded carrots

1 tablespoon minced parsley

2 teaspoons minced fresh dill

1 cup yogurt or kefir

½ teaspoon dry mustard

1. Peel the cucumbers, cut them in half lengthwise, and use a teaspoon to remove the seeds. Slice the cucumbers thinly into half moons.
2. Place the cucumbers in a medium-size serving bowl.
3. Add the scallions, peppers or carrots, parsley and dill and toss gently to combine.
4. Whisk the dry mustard into the yogurt or kefir and then toss the dressing with the cucumber mixture.
5. Refrigerate until serving time.

About 4 cups

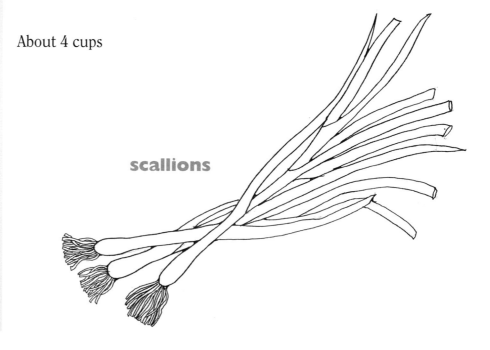

scallions

Do Ahead

- Cook the chicken or tempeh up to a day ahead of time.

- Wash and prepare your vegetables up to two days ahead of time.

- Make the Coconut Almond Dressing up to two days ahead of time.

Chinese Vegetable Salad with Coconut Almond Dressing

8 – 12 ounces boneless skinless chicken breast
~ or ~ 8 – 12 ounces tempeh

½ cup almond butter

½ cup coconut milk

¼ cup rice vinegar

1 tablespoon mirin

2 ½ tablespoons tamari

2 tablespoons toasted sesame oil

2 teaspoons fresh ginger, minced

¼ – ½ teaspoons chili flakes

Dash sea salt

1 small head Napa, Savoy or green cabbage, very thinly sliced, 4 to 5 cups

1 carrot, grated

1 handful of sugar snap or snow peas, strings removed and cut in half diagonally

½ cucumber, peeled, cut in half lengthwise and seeded, then cut into thin slices on the diagonal

1 small red, yellow or orange bell pepper, seeded and thinly sliced

½ cup roasted cashews or peanuts

Cilantro (optional)

Chinese Vegetable Salad

1. If you are using chicken, preheat the oven to 375° and bake the chicken in a small pan for 20 to 25 minutes, or until it is cooked through. Cool and then slice it thinly.

2. If you are using tempeh, steam it for about five minutes, and then set it aside to cool. When the tempeh is cool enough to handle, dice it into bite-sized cubes. Heat a large skillet with a tablespoon or so of olive oil. When the skillet is hot, add the tempeh and cook over medium high heat, turning every few minutes until the tempeh is golden brown on all sides. Sprinkle 1 tablespoon of tamari over the tempeh and swirl the pan to coat evenly. Set tempeh aside.

3. To make the dressing, place the almond butter, coconut milk, rice vinegar, tamari, sesame oil, ginger and crushed red chilies in a blender and blend until the dressing is smooth. Taste and add more chilies, more ginger or more rice vinegar as needed.

4. Toss the vegetables in a large bowl. Add your chicken or tempeh and enough dressing to coat everything lightly. Garnish with the cashews or peanuts and cilantro leaves.

5. Serve with the remaining dressing on the side.

Serves 4

Tips

- Like many of our salads, the mix of vegetables is really up to you. Feel free to add, subtract and substitute to suit your fancy, the season or what's available in your refrigerator.

- Mix all the vegetables and keep them in a bag or bowl in your refrigerator. Make the dressing and store it in a small jar. Cook and slice the chicken and store it in a covered container. When you are hungry, put a bit of everything in a bowl and enjoy!

- Almonds and coconut milk are two excellent sources of healthy fats, an important part of the diet for folks who are trying to keep weight on during chemotherapy and radiation treatments.

Variation

Use any leftover Almond Coconut Dressing with brown rice and steamed vegetables or as a dip for raw vegetables.

Kale Salad with Arame & Sesame Seeds

I cup arame seaweed, soaked in plenty of warm water for about 15 minutes

2 bunches curly or Tuscan kale, leaves removed from the stems and sliced very thinly

2 carrots, shredded

3 scallions, sliced very thinly on the diagonal

2 tablespoons sesame seeds

3 tablespoons toasted sesame oil

3 tablespoons umeboshi plum vinegar

1. Bring a pot of water to a boil, add the shredded kale and cook until just tender, about 5 minutes or so. Drain the kale and rinse under cold water, then drain very well, squeezing out as much water as you can, and place it in a large bowl. The kale will be very compressed at this point so take a minute and fluff it back up by pulling it apart.

2. Drain the arame and press out as much water as you can. Add the arame to the kale and toss well.

3. Whisk together the sesame oil and umeboshi vinegar.

4. Add the carrots, scallions, sesame seeds and dressing, and toss everything together with your hands or a spoon.

Makes 4 – 5 cups

Do Ahead

• The kale, carrots and scallions can be washed and prepared up to a day ahead of time.

• You can cook the kale up to a day ahead of time, and also soak and drain your arame.

Tips

• For a twist on this salad, omit the carrots and scallions. Add one or two small beets, peeled and shredded, along with ¼ cup or so of dried cranberries.

• Arame can seem expensive when you buy it in 1 or 2 ounce bags at the grocery store. But a little goes a long way and sea vegetables like arame are one of the most concentrated forms of important minerals. Look in the Resource Guide for more cost effective mail order sources of sea vegetables like arame and kombu. We recommend eating some form of sea vegetables at least once a week.

About Umeboshi Plums

Umeboshi plums are prized in Asian cultures for their ability to lessen fatigue, stimulate digestion and promote the elimination of toxins from the body. Umeboshi plums are one of the most alkalinizing foods you can eat; even the vinegar is alkaline. In Japan, an umeboshi a day is regarded as one of the best preventive medicines available.

Raw Tuscan Kale Salad with Garlic & Lemon

This salad is really delicious and requires no cooking. Try it on one of those warm summer days when you don't want to turn on your stove.

Do Ahead

- The kale can be prepared a day ahead of time.

- You can grate the cheese and squeeze the lemon juice a day ahead of time.

1 bunch kale, Tuscan or Lacinato preferred but really any kale will do!

¼ cup coarse fresh bread crumbs, diced small and then crumbled between your fingers

½ clove garlic, pressed in a garlic press, or finely minced

¼ cup grated Pecorino, Romano or Asiago cheese

3 tablespoons olive oil

2 – 3 tablespoons fresh lemon juice

¼ teaspoon sea salt

pepper to taste

1. Remove the kale leaves from the stems and then slice the kale into thin ribbons. Place in a large bowl.
2. Combine the garlic with the cheese, olive oil, lemon juice, sea salt and pepper and whisk until it is creamy.
3. Pour the dressing over the kale and toss well.
4. Garnish the salad with bread crumbs, additional cheese and a drizzle of olive oil.

Makes 5 – 6 cups

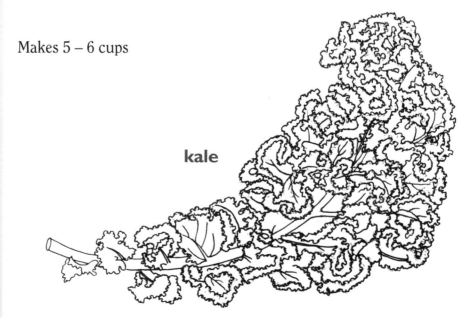

kale

Herb Marinated Vegetable Salad

Optional Additions

You can add a wide variety of other vegetables to this salad, including but certainly not limited to the following suggestions:

- Green beans, trimmed and cut in 1" lengths and steamed until crisp tender

- Asparagus, trimmed and cut in 1" lengths and steamed until crisp tender

- Broccoli or cauliflower florets, steamed until crisp tender

- Beets, cut in quarters, steamed until tender and then peeled and sliced

Feel free to reduce or omit the artichoke hearts, tomatoes, olives and/or red onion!

Other delicious additions include hard-boiled eggs, canned or fresh salmon or tuna, and cooked shrimp.

6 cups Yukon Gold potatoes, scrubbed and then boiled until just tender

6 ounces marinated artichoke hearts, drained and sliced

1 cup cherry tomatoes, halved

~ or ~ 1 small red bell pepper, diced or sliced and sautéed briefly

½ cup Nicoise or Kalamata olives, pitted and halved

½ cup fresh parsley, chopped

¼ cup fresh basil, chopped

¼ cup fresh dill, chopped

¼ – ½ red onion, sliced very thinly (optional)

3 tablespoons red wine vinegar

zest and juice of one lemon

1 tablespoon Dijon mustard

¼ teaspoon each sea salt and pepper, or to taste

8 – 9 tablespoons olive oil

2 tablespoons capers, drained

1. While the potatoes are cooking, whisk together the red wine vinegar, lemon juice and zest, Dijon, sea salt, olive oil and capers and set aside.

2. When the potatoes are tender, rinse them under cold water, drain well and refrigerate to help cool. When they are cool enough to handle, cut them into wedges or dice them, and toss them with a small amount of the dressing.

3. Add the rest of the ingredients, any additional steamed vegetables, and as much dressing as you need. Toss to coat evenly.

Makes 6 – 8 cups

Beet, Barley & Arugula Salad

I pound beets, trimmed and quartered

I ¼ cups barley, soaked 4 hours or overnight, then drained

4 cups water

I small piece kombu

I bunch arugula, washed and roughly chopped, about 4 to 5 cups

¼ cup walnuts or pecans, toasted

¼ cup balsamic vinegar

2 tablespoons olive oil

2 teaspoons fennel seeds

½ teaspoon sea salt

I – 4-ounce package crumbled feta cheese or goat cheese, (optional)

1. Place the beets in a saucepan, cover with water and bring to a boil. Simmer, partially covered, until the beets are tender when poked with a fork, about 15 to 20 minutes depending on the size and age of your beets. When they are tender, drain and rinse under cold water. When the beets are cool enough to handle, slip the skins off and slice the beets into wedges. Set aside.

2. While the beets are cooking, bring the water, barley and kombu to a boil. Reduce the heat to low, cover and cook for 20 – 25 minutes or until the barley is tender. Drain, rinse under cold water and drain again. Place the barley in a large bowl.

3. Whisk together the balsamic vinegar, olive oil, fennel seeds and sea salt. Toss the dressing with the barley, then add the beets, arugula, toasted walnuts and, if desired, the cheese. Toss gently to combine.

Makes about 2 quarts of salad

Do Ahead

• The barley and beets can be cooked a day ahead of time.

• The dressing can be made a day ahead of time.

• The walnuts can be toasted a couple of days ahead of time.

How to Toast Nuts

Preheat your oven to 350˚. Place the nuts in a small baking pan. Roast them until they are fragrant and starting to brown. This will take anywhere from 6 to 12 minutes depending on the nuts and your oven. Watch carefully, though, as nuts can burn quickly! You can also toast nuts in a heavy-bottomed skillet over low heat, stirring the nuts often. This will take 6 to 10 minutes. Don't try to hurry things – you want to toast the nuts all the way through, not simply get them brown on the outside.

Fruity Quinoa Salad

Do Ahead

There isn't much to prep for this salad, but you can chop the apricots, toast the pine nuts and dice the red onion up to a day ahead of time.

Tip

Try this wonderful salad if you need breakfast on the go. It's packed with fiber, protein and a host of beneficial vitamins and phytonutrients.

1 cup quinoa, soaked for at least an hour or overnight, then rinsed well in a mesh colander

½ cup water

½ cup orange juice

1 tablespoon olive oil

⅓ cup dried apricots, diced

1 tablespoon dried goji berries

1 tablespoon golden or regular raisins

2 teaspoons fresh ginger, grated

¼ to ½ cup red onion, finely diced

½ tablespoon mirin

2 tablespoons pine nuts, toasted

2 tablespoons minced fresh cilantro (optional)

1. Bring the water, orange juice and olive oil to a boil. Add the quinoa, dried fruit and ginger. Cover, reduce the heat to low, and cook for 10 to 15 minutes, or until all the water is absorbed and the quinoa is tender. Let it sit covered for five minutes.

2. Bring a small pot of water to a boil and add the diced red onion. Cook for 15 seconds and then drain well and toss with the mirin to bring out its pink color. (Feel free to skip this step and simply add a bit of minced raw onion to your salad.)

3. When the quinoa is tender, turn it out into a bowl. Add the onions and toasted pine nuts and fluff together gently with a fork. If you like, garnish with a bit of chopped cilantro.

4. Serve warm or at room temperature.

Serves 2 – 3

Millet & Aduki Bean Salad with Lemon Dressing

1 cup millet

2 cups boiling water

Pinch of sea salt

2 cups cooked aduki beans or 1 14-ounce can aduki beans, drained and rinsed

½ cup red onion, diced and sautéed briefly

1 cup fresh corn, cut from the cob and sautéed for a minute or two, or frozen corn, thawed, or 1 cup peeled, seeded and diced cucumber

1 pint cherry tomatoes, cut in half

½ cup fresh parsley, chopped

4 tablespoons olive oil

Zest of one lemon

4 tablespoons fresh lemon juice

½ teaspoon ground cumin

½ teaspoon sea salt

Fresh ground pepper to taste

1. Toast the millet in a saucepan over medium heat, stirring constantly, until it begins to brown and gives off a nutty fragrance. Carefully add the boiling water and the sea salt, reduce the heat to low and cover. Cook until the water is absorbed and the millet is tender, 20 to 25 minutes.

2. Turn the millet out onto a cookie sheet and spread it out to cool.

3. While the millet is cooling, whisk together the olive oil, lemon juice and zest, cumin, sea salt and pepper for the dressing. Prepare the remaining ingredients.

4. When the millet is cool, crumble it into a bowl and toss with the dressing. Add the remaining ingredients and toss again to mix everything evenly.

Makes about 6 cups

Do Ahead

- The millet and beans can be washed a day ahead of time.

- The dressing can be made a day ahead of time.

Tip

To cook aduki beans from scratch, soak ⅔ cup of beans overnight in about 4 cups water. Drain, rinse and place in a saucepan with about 3 cups of water. Bring to a boil, reduce the heat to a simmer, and cook until the beans are tender, testing after about 25 minutes. After that, check every 5 minutes or so to make sure your beans don't get overcooked and turn mushy.

About Millet

Millet is an excellent source of iron and magnesium and it is also high in calcium, phosphorous, manganese, zinc and B vitamins. It has the highest iron content of any grain except amaranth and quinoa. The natural alkalinity of millet makes it easily digestible, so it is very beneficial for people with ulcers and digestive problems. It is believed to be one of the least allergenic of all grains.

Do Ahead

- All of the vegetables can be washed and chopped up to two days ahead of time.

- The dressing will keep for up to a week in the refrigerator.

- Cook the millet and steam the broccoli the day before or in the morning.

Variation

Feel free to use a different grain in any of the grain salads – millet, quinoa, couscous and bulgur wheat all exchange pretty easily. For rice salads, try all wild rice or all brown basmati, or try barley, kamut or wheat berries.

Broccoli & Millet Salad with Toasted Cashews

1 cup millet

¼ teaspoon sea salt

2 cups boiling water

2 cups broccoli, florets and chopped stems

1 teaspoon minced garlic

¾ cup thinly sliced celery

1 cup cherry tomatoes, sliced in half

¼ cup minced fresh dill weed

¼ cup minced fresh parsley

½ – 1 cup cashews, toasted

⅓ cup fresh lemon juice

⅓ cup olive oil

½ teaspoon sea salt

1. Toast the millet in a saucepan over medium heat, stirring constantly, until it begins to brown and gives off a nutty fragrance. Carefully add the boiling water and the sea salt, reduce the heat to low and cover. Cook until the water is absorbed and the millet is tender, 20 to 25 minutes.

2. Put the millet on a cookie sheet and spread it out to cool.

3. While the millet is cooling, steam the broccoli just until tender and bright green. Rinse under cold water, drain well and place in a large bowl.

4. Add the celery, tomatoes, dill and parsley to the broccoli.

5. In a separate bowl, whisk together the lemon juice, olive oil and sea salt.

6. When the millet is cool, crumble it into the vegetables. Add the cashews and the dressing and toss everything together.

Makes 7 – 8 cups

Bulgur Wheat Salad with Cucumbers & Fresh Herbs (Tabouli)

¾ cup bulgur wheat or couscous

¾ cup boiling water

3 tablespoons fresh lemon juice

3 tablespoons olive oil

I teaspoon minced garlic

¼ – ½ teaspoon sea salt, to taste

I large cucumber, peeled, seeded and diced into ¼ inch pieces

3 scallions, trimmed and thinly sliced

I bunch fresh parsley, minced

I bunch fresh mint, minced

Optional ingredients

½ pint cherry tomatoes, halved, or I medium tomato, diced

I cup cooked garbanzo beans

1. Place the bulgur wheat or couscous in a large bowl and pour boiling water over it. Let it sit for 20 minutes or until all the water is absorbed and the grain is tender, then fluff with a fork.
2. Whisk together the lemon juice, olive oil, garlic and sea salt. Pour dressing over the grains and toss to combine well. Let sit for at least 30 minutes.
3. Add the remaining ingredients and toss again.

Serves 4

Do Ahead

- The grains can be prepared up to a day ahead of time, or in the morning.

- Mix your dressing up to a day ahead.

Tips

- To seed cucumbers, cut them in half lengthwise and then use a teaspoon to scrape out the seeds from each half.

- If you have a food processor, rinse the herbs, spin them dry, and then chop them in the food processor.

Variation

If you are avoiding wheat, make this salad with quinoa. Rinse ¾ cup quinoa well and then soak for at least 1 hour and preferably overnight. Place the quinoa in a small pot with about ¾ cup of water. Bring to a boil, reduce the heat to very low and cover. The quinoa will take about 8 to 10 minutes depending on how long it soaked. It's done when the grains are tender and all the water is absorbed.

Rice Noodle Extravaganza

4 ounces Asian rice noodles*
  (this makes about 3½ cups cooked noodles)

Do Ahead

- This dressing will keep happily in your fridge for up to a week. Shake well before using!

- Cook off the rice noodles, drain well under cool water, and then toss with half the dressing. Store in the refrigerator and add optional ingredients when you are ready to eat.

- Any vegetables can be prepared a day or two ahead of time.

Variations

- The potential of this salad is as limitless as your imagination. Adding some sliced sautéed shiitake mushrooms, steamed broccoli florets and a bit of sliced cooked chicken or shrimp turns it into a main dish. If you want to use it as a side dish but want it to be more colorful and nutritious, add ½ to 1 cup each of two to four vegetables, either lightly steamed or sautéed until tender. Some great possibilities are shiitakes, thinly sliced carrot, thinly sliced zucchini or other summer squash, broccoli, sliced sautéed red, yellow or orange bell peppers, sugar snap or snow peas, bok choy or Napa cabbage. You can cook all of the vegetables or leave some raw for their crunch factor.

- Rice noodles are also delicious with the Coconut Almond Sauce (see page 76).

* Asian rice noodles are available in the Asian section of most grocery stores or in Asian markets. They are very thin white noodles made from rice flour.

Dressing
  Whisk together:

2 talespoons toasted sesame oil

2 tablespoons tamari or Bragg's Aminos

1½ tablespoon rice vinegar

1 tablespoon maple syrup or brown rice syrup

1 – 2 teaspoons minced ginger

Optional Suggestions

2 – 4 cups steamed, sautéed or raw vegetables of choice
  (see Variations to the left)

4 – 8 ounces chicken, tempeh, or shrimp

2 – 4 tablespoons toasted sesame seeds, cashews or peanuts

Thinly sliced scallions or whole cilantro leaves

1. Bring a large pot of water to a boil. Add the noodles and use tongs or a fork to pull the strands apart so that they don't stick together. The noodles will take about 3 to 4 minutes. As soon as they taste tender, drain them and rinse well with cool water, then drain well.
2. Toss the noodles with about half the dressing.
3. Add any other vegetables or protein you want along with as much dressing as needed to moisten and flavor everything.
4. Garnish as desired with toasted sesame seeds or nuts, sliced scallions or cilantro leaves.

Makes 3½ – 5 cups depending on what you add

Sprouted Quinoa Salad

1 cup quinoa, soaked overnight, rinsed and then sprouted for 1 – 2 days (see sprouting instructions on page 54)

½ cup vegetable or chicken broth

¼ cup goji berries, soaked if you prefer

⅛ cup arame, soaked in warm water for 10 – 15 minutes, then drained well

2 green onions, chopped

½ cup carrots, grated or chopped

⅓ cup red, yellow or orange bell bepper, diced

⅓ cup celery, finely chopped

1 tablespoon chopped fresh parsley

3 tablespoons chopped fresh mint

3 tablespoons toasted sunflower and/or pumpkin seeds

Dressing

1½ tablespoons toasted sesame oil

2 teaspoons balsamic vinegar

2 teaspoons ground cumin

1 teaspoon ground coriander

Sea salt to taste

1. In a small saucepan, warm the broth and add the sprouted quinoa. Cover and simmer for 10 minutes.
2. While the quinoa is cooking, whisk together the dressing ingredients and then set aside.
3. When the quinoa is cooked, put it in a bowl to cool. Add the dressing, arame and goji berries and toss to combine.
4. Let the quinoa cool completely and then add the rest of the vegetables, the herbs and the toasted seeds.

Makes 4 – 5 cups

Do Ahead

- The dressing will keep in the refrigerator for up to a week.

- You can prepare the quinoa up to a day ahead of time.

- All the vegetables can be prepared up to a day ahead of time.

Tip

This salad can also be made with regular quinoa or with any other grain.

About Quinoa

Quinoa is an ancient grain that is gluten-free and one of the least allergenic grains available. It is a good source of protein, containing all the essential amino acids needed to build and maintain your body. Quinoa provides an excellent source of magnesium, calcium and manganese. It also provides vitamin B_2 and vitamin E as well as dietary fiber, iron, phosphorous, copper and zinc. Soak the quinoa overnight to remove the saponins and allow for better digestion of the grain.

Wild Rice Salad with Grapes & Pecans

Do Ahead

- The brown rice and wild rice can both be cooked up to a day ahead of time.

- You can whisk the dressing ingredients together and store in the refrigerator for up to a week.

- The grapes, scallions and parsley can be washed and chopped in the morning.

Tip

While there is already plenty of protein in this salad, feel free to add a bit of diced cooked chicken, turkey or tempeh if you need more protein in your diet.

1¼ cup brown basmati rice,
    soaked for at least one hour or overnight
½ cup wild rice (wild rice does not need to be soaked)

⅓ cup olive oil
⅓ cup lemon juice
1 teaspoon sea salt
1 tablespoon honey, maple syrup, or brown rice syrup

1 bunch scallions, trimmed and thinly sliced
¾ cup minced fresh parsley
1 cup toasted pecans or walnuts
1½ cups red and or green grapes, cut in half
1 cup cooked garbanzo beans (optional)

1. Drain the rice and then place it in a small saucepan with 1¾ cups water and ¼ teaspoon sea salt. Bring it to a boil, reduce the heat to low, cover and cook until the rice is tender and all the water is absorbed, 25 to 30 minutes. Put the rice in a large bowl to cool.

2. In another saucepan, cover the wild rice with about 2 cups of water. Bring to a boil, reduce heat to low and simmer until wild rice is tender, about 30 to 35 minutes. Drain rice well and add to the brown rice.

3. Whisk together the olive oil, lemon juice, sea salt and honey until the honey is incorporated and the dressing is thick.

4. When the rice has cooled, add the dressing and toss to coat. Then add the remaining ingredients and toss everything together.

Makes 7 – 8 cups

scallions

Wild Rice Salad with Winter Squash & Cranberries

½ cup brown Basmati rice, soaked for at least one hour or overnight, then drained

½ cup wild rice (does not need to be soaked)

2 cups peeled, diced winter squash – Delicata or Butternut

2 stalks celery, diced

3 green onions, sliced very thinly

½ cup diced red, yellow or orange bell pepper (optional)

¼ – ½ cup fresh parsley, chopped

¼ cup dried cranberries or goji berries

¼ – ½ cup pecans or walnuts, toasted

¼ cup olive oil

¼ cup apple cider vinegar

1 – 2 tablespoons honey or brown rice syrup

¾ teaspoon ground sage

½ teaspoon sea salt

½ teaspoon black pepper

1. Put the brown rice in a small saucepan with a dash of sea salt and 1 cup water. Bring to a boil, cover, and reduce the heat to low. Cook for 30 to 40 minutes or until the rice is tender and all the liquid is absorbed. Put it in a bowl to cool.

2. Place the wild rice in a pot with 2 cups of water. Bring to a boil, reduce the heat to medium low and cook uncovered at a gentle boil until the rice is tender, about 30 to 45 minutes. When the wild rice is tender, drain and add it to the brown rice.

3. While the rice is cooking, preheat the oven to 400°. Toss the Delicata or other cubed squash with a bit of olive oil. Place it in a baking pan and roast until just tender when pierced with a fork, about 15 to 20 minutes. You can also steam the squash in a steamer basket until tender, 5 to 8 minutes. At the same time, roast your pecans or walnuts on a small baking pan for 6 to 8 minutes, or just until they are fragrant and starting to color. Watch nuts carefully as they can burn quickly!

4. Whisk the dressing ingredients together, then taste and add more sea salt, apple cider vinegar and/or sweetener.

5. When the rice has cooled slightly, toss with the dressing and add the remaining ingredients, stirring to combine evenly.

Makes 6 – 7 cups

Do Ahead

- The vegetables can all be washed and chopped up to two days ahead of time.

- The dressing can be made up to two days ahead of time.

- Roast the squash and toast the nuts up to a day ahead of time.

- Cook off the rice a day ahead of time or in the morning.

Variations

- This salad can be eaten warm or cold. Adding cooked, diced chicken, turkey or tempeh turns this into a main dish.

- Feel free to make the salad with all brown rice or all wild rice. Both are wonderful.

Edamame & Orange Salad

2 cups frozen shelled edamame beans

3 red radishes, trimmed and diced

½ cup diced seeded cucumber

½ cup chopped red, yellow or orange bell pepper

¼ cup chopped scallions, white and green parts

1 orange

2 tablespoons olive oil

2 tablespoons rice vinegar

2 tablespoons orange juice, preferably fresh

2 teaspoons tamari

Sea salt and freshly ground black pepper, to taste

¼ cup cilantro leaves, chopped

1. In a large pot of boiling water, cook the edamame according to package directions. Drain in a colander, running cold water over the beans to cool them. Drain well and transfer the edamame to a mixing bowl.

2. Add the radishes, cucumber, red pepper and scallions. Toss lightly to mix.

3. Grate 2 teaspoons zest from the orange and set aside. Cut off the top and bottom of the orange. Setting the orange on one of its cut sides on your work surface, slice off the peel in strips, letting the knife follow the curve of the fruit. Cut the orange into sections and arrange on top of the salad.

4. In a small bowl, whisk together the orange zest with the vinegar, tamari, oil and orange juice. Season to taste with sea salt and pepper. Drizzle the dressing over the salad. Sprinkle cilantro on top and serve.

Makes 4 servings

Do Ahead

- Cook the edamame up to a day ahead of time.

- Wash and chop your vegetables up to a day ahead of time.

About Edamame

Edamame or fresh soybeans, are an excellent source of protein, fiber, calcium, iron, phosphorus and molybdenum. They also provide vitamins B_1, B_2, B_6, E and folic acid. Phytoestrogens, protease inhibitors and phytosterols in edamame help protect against increased cholesterol, support the immune system, and may inhibit some types of cancer. Fresh soybeans last about two days in the refrigerator. If they are frozen, use them within five months.

About Soy Foods

Please note that some people should be careful about eating regular amounts of any soy product such as edamame. The reason is that soy has oxalates which may stimulate kidney stones and compounds that may inhibit thyroid function. Those with estrogen-sensitive breast tumors also want to limit their intake of soy to no more than two three- or four-ounce servings per week. Please consult your physician before eating edamame or other soy products on a regular basis.

Lentil Salad with Variations

Do Ahead

- The lentils can be cooked up to a day ahead of time.

- The dressing will keep for up to a week in the refrigerator.

- Any of the vegetables or herbs can be washed and chopped up to a day ahead of time, and sautéed as well.

1¼ cup dried French green lentils

3 tablespoons balsamic vinegar

3 tablespoons olive oil

1 tablespoon fresh lemon juice

1 tablespoon red wine vinegar

1 clove garlic, minced

¼ teaspoon sea salt

¼ teaspoon pepper

1. Sort through the lentils to make sure there are no little stones. Put them in a sauce pan and cover with 4 cups of water. Bring to a boil, reduce the heat to a gentle simmer, and cook the lentils for about 18 to 20 minutes, until just tender. Begin checking them at about 15 minutes to be sure they don't get mushy and begin falling apart.

2. While the lentils are cooking, whisk together the remaining ingredients and set aside.

3. As soon as the lentils are tender and before they become mushy, drain them well and place in a medium sized bowl. Add the dressing, toss to coat, and let the lentils marinate for a bit while you finish preparing whatever other vegetables you are adding.

4. When the lentils have cooled, add the remaining ingredients for whichever version you are making. Toss to combine everything evenly and serve.

Makes about 6 cups

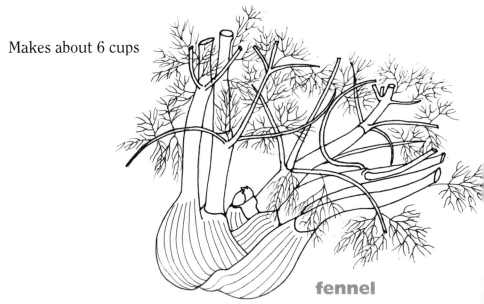

fennel

Lentil Salad with Variations

Lentil Salad with Beets, Oranges & Toasted Walnuts

2 small beets, baked or boiled until tender, then peeled and diced

1 small fennel bulb, trimmed, cored and diced

1 orange, peeled and sectioned, and each section cut in half

2 – 4 tablespoons minced fresh parsley

2 – 4 tablespoons minced fresh dill

¼ – ½ cup toasted walnuts

2 – 4 ounces goat cheese, crumbled (optional)

Use orange juice instead of lemon juice in the dressing and add some of the orange zest as well.

Lentil Salad with Artichokes

6 ounces marinated artichokes, drained and sliced

½ red, yellow or orange bell pepper, diced and sautéed briefly

~ or ~ 1 cup cherry tomatoes cut in half

½ small red onion, diced and sautéed with the bell pepper

2 – 4 tablespoons toasted pine nuts

½ cup minced fresh parsley

2 – 4 ounces feta cheese, diced or crumbled (optional)

Summer Lentil Salad

1 cucumber, peeled, seeded and diced

½ cup cherry or grape tomatoes, cut in half

½ cup diced red, yellow or orange bell pepper

2 – 3 tablespoons minced red onion

½ cup mixed fresh herbs – parsley, dill, basil or mint

2 – 4 ounces feta or goat cheese, crumbled (optional)

Mediterranean Lentil & Quinoa Salad

This salad is a complete meal on a warm summer evening, or a wonderful food to snack on throughout the day.

½ cup French green lentils

1 cup quinoa, soaked at least one hour or overnight, then rinsed well under cold water

¾ cups water

¼ teaspoon sea salt

1 cup cherry tomatoes, halved

1 bunch arugula, leaves washed, spun dry and roughly chopped, about 3 – 4 cups

½ cup finely chopped fresh mint

½ cup crumbled feta cheese (optional)

2 tablespoons olive oil

2 tablespoons white wine vinegar

2 teaspoons lemon zest

2 tablespoons lemon juice

1 clove garlic minced

¼ teaspoon sea salt

1. Cover the lentils generously with water and bring to a boil. Reduce the heat to a gentle simmer and cook just until tender, about 15 to 20 minutes. Test them often and drain them as soon as the lentils are al dente. Rinse under cool water, drain well and put in a large bowl to cool.

2. While the lentils are cooling, place the quinoa, water and sea salt in a small saucepan and bring to a boil. Reduce the heat to very low, cover, and cook for 10 to 12 minutes until the quinoa is tender and the water is absorbed. Add to the lentils and cool completely, stirring every so often.

3. For the dressing, whisk together the olive oil, vinegar, lemon juice and zest, garlic and sea salt.

4. When the quinoa and lentils are cool, add the dressing and toss to coat. Stir in the cherry tomatoes, arugula, mint and, if desired, the feta and combine evenly.

Do Ahead

- The lentils and quinoa can be cooked up to a day ahead of time.

- The dressing will keep for a week in the refrigerator.

- The cherry tomatoes, arugula and mint can be prepared in the morning.

Makes 5 – 6 cups

Sprouted Bean Salad with Sesame Mustard Dressing

Do Ahead

- The dressing will keep in the refrigerator for up to a week.

- You can wash and chop the vegetables and herbs in the morning.

Sprouting Instructions

Fill a large bowl with 1½ cups dried lentils or mung beans and cover them with water. Set the bowl in a dark place over night. In the morning, place the lentils in a mesh basket or strainer and rinse them well. Set them back in a dark place. Continue rinsing them twice each day, in the morning and at night. Sprouting will take 3 to 4 days, depending on the temperature and dampness. The sprouts are ready when the beans have ¼ inch long tails.

2½ cups sprouted French lentils or mung beans

2 cups carrots, scrubbed or peeled and grated

2 cups cabbage, very thinly sliced
~ or ~ 2 cups peeled, grated beets

1 cup goji berries (or cranberries or golden raisins)

1½ cups sunflower or pumpkin seeds

¾ cup chopped fresh cilantro

½ cup chopped fresh parsley

¼ cup chopped fresh mint

½ cup toasted sesame oil

⅓ cup Balsamic vinegar

1 teaspoon Dijon mustard

½ teaspoon sea salt

1. Place the carrots in a bowl and toss with lemon juice to prevent browning. Layer in the following order: the cabbage or beets over the carrots; the mung beans over the cabbage or beets; the goji berries and then the seeds. Garnish with cilantro, parsley and mint.

2. Whisk together the sesame oil, balsamic vinegar, Dijon mustard and sea salt. Drizzle the dressing over the salad, toss and serve.

Serves 4 – 6

Do Ahead

- The dressing will keep in the refrigerator for up to a week.

- The beans can be cooked a day ahead of time.

- Any vegetables can be washed, chopped and steamed or sautéed up to a day ahead of time.

White Bean Salad with Seasonal Variations

Beans

1 cup Great Northern white beans, soaked overnight in 4 cups water
~ or ~ 2 14-ounce cans white beans, rinsed and drained

2 bay leaves

1 teaspoon dried thyme, or several fresh sprigs

2 cloves garlic, smashed

¾ teaspoon sea salt

Dressing

3 tablespoons olive oil

1 teaspoon lemon zest

1 tablespoon + 1 teaspoon lemon juice

1 – 2 cloves garlic, minced

¼ teaspoon sea salt

Black pepper to taste

Summer Salad

⅓ pound fresh green beans, stem end trimmed off and cut in 1" pieces

2 medium to large tomatoes, cut in wedges, or a pint of cherry or sungold tomatoes, halved

⅛ red onion, sliced very thinly in half moons or minced

4 tablespoons fresh basil, slivered or chopped

Spring Salad

1 small bunch fresh asparagus, trimmed, sliced on the diagonal about 1" and steamed just until tender

¼ – ½ small head radicchio, sliced thinly

¼ cup red onion, minced

2 – 3 tablespoons fresh dill, minced

White Bean Salad

Fall/Winter Salad

I red onion, thinly sliced and sautéed until very tender in
  I tablespoon olive oil

¼ – ½ cup marinated sun-dried tomatoes, drained and
  thinly sliced

½ cup fresh chopped parsley

6 ounces marinated artichoke hearts, drained and sliced

¼ cup Kalamata or Nicoise olives, cut in half and pitted

Replace the lemon juice and lemon zest with balsamic vinegar
  and add I teaspoon Dijon mustard.

1. Drain the beans and then put them in a medium-sized sauce
   pan with fresh water to cover by about an inch. Add the bay leaf,
   thyme, garlic and 1 teaspoon of sea salt. Bring the beans to a
   gentle boil, reduce the heat, and simmer gently with the lid off.
   Watch your beans closely and test them starting at about 25 or
   30 minutes. The cooking time can vary widely depending on
   how fresh your beans are. If they are really fresh, the cooking
   time can be as little as 30 to 40 minutes, but some may need an
   hour or more.

2. While the beans are cooking, whisk together the dressing
   ingredients and set aside.

3. Steam or sauté any vegetables that need to be cooked, and
   prepare the rest of the ingredients.

4. When the beans are done, drain them and remove the bay
   leaf, pieces of garlic and thyme stems. Toss the beans with the
   dressing and let them cool.

5. Add the remaining ingredients and toss to mix well. Taste and
   adjust the seasonings with more sea salt, garlic or lemon.

Makes 5 – 6 cups

asparagus

Tips

- To test whether or not dried beans are
  tender, take two or three out of the pot
  and let them cool for several minutes
  before tasting. The beans should be
  completely tender but still hold their
  shape.

- Feel free to substitute two cans of
  cooked beans, drained and rinsed.

Chapter 5•Nourishing Soups

RECIPES

**Miso Ginger Soup
with Soba Noodles**

Basic "Creamy" Vegetable Soup with Broccoli

½ tablespoon olive oil

I cup chopped onion

½ cup chopped carrot

I cup chopped potato (scrubbed or peeled)

3 – 4 cups chopped broccoli, florets and peeled stems

3 cups Immune Broth, Chicken Bone Broth,
   or vegetable or chicken stock, or water

½ – ¾ cup dairy or non-dairy milk (optional)

I teaspoon sea salt

2 tablespoons fresh dill, chopped, or I teaspoon dried

1. Heat the olive oil in a 2-quart sauce pan. Add the chopped onions and sauté until tender, about 5 to 7 minutes, stirring every so often.
2. Add the carrots, potatoes, and broth, stock or water to the onions along with half the sea salt. Bring to a boil, reduce the heat to low, and simmer, covered, about 10 minutes or until the vegetables are almost tender. Add the broccoli and continue cooking just until it is tender, another 5 minutes or so.
3. Let the soup cool slightly, then working in batches carefully purée it in a blender until smooth and velvety.
4. Return the soup to the saucepan and stir in enough milk of your choice to make it the right thickness for you, along with the dill. Taste and adjust the seasonings, adding enough sea salt to suit your taste buds.

Makes 7 – 8 cups

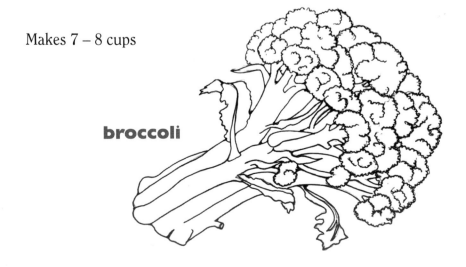

broccoli

Do Ahead

All of the vegetables for this soup can be washed and chopped up to two days ahead of time. Store the potatoes covered in cold water to prevent browning and keep everything in your refrigerator until you are ready to cook.

Variations

You can use this basic recipe to make a variety of creamy vegetable soups. Try substituting any of the following for the broccoli: 1 bunch asparagus, trimmed and chopped; 3 cups chopped cauliflower; 3 cups chopped zucchini or other summer squash, or ten ounces fresh spinach leaves (1 bunch cleaned well). If you are using the spinach, add it at the very end of the cooking and just let it wilt before puréeing your soup.

Tips

- If you are puréeing a soup, don't worry about chopping your ingredients into small pieces. They will take a bit longer to cook if they are larger but you will save yourself some time and effort and, once the soup is puréed, it won't matter how big the pieces were!

- For soups that won't be puréed, use your food processor to help with the chopping. Cut vegetables into chunks, maybe 2" or so in size. Place in the processor and use the on/off pulse to chop them until they are the size that you want, from a rough chop to minced.

Carrot Soup with Ginger & Cashews

Do Ahead

- The onions, carrots and ginger can all be prepared up to two days ahead of time and stored in your refrigerator.

- The soup can be cooked in the morning and then left, covered, on your stove to cool. Then purée later, reheat what you want to eat and refrigerate or freeze the rest.

- If you have a food processor, use it to slice the carrots very thinly. This will help them cook more quickly and save your energy as well.

Tips

- Consider keeping organic bottled lime and lemon juice on hand in your refrigerator so that it's easy for you to add these bright flavors to your cooking.

- Be careful when blending hot soup. Start blending on the lowest setting, increase the speed slowly, and don't fill the blender more than halfway. Hot food will expand under the pressure of the blender.

6 cups carrots, peeled or scrubbed and sliced

8 cups Immune Broth, Chicken Bone Broth, or vegetable or chicken stock, or water

1½ teaspoons sea salt

1 tablespoon olive oil

1½ cups chopped onion

4 tablespoons fresh ginger, peeled and minced

¼ cup orange juice

1 tablespoon lime juice

¾ cup raw cashews

¼ cup cilantro, minced

1. Put the carrots, water and sea salt in a large saucepan and bring to a boil. Turn the heat down to a simmer, partially cover, and cook the carrots until they are very tender, about twenty minutes.

2. While the carrots are cooking, heat the olive oil in a skillet and sauté the onion and ginger over medium heat until they are tender but not browned. This should take 5 to 7 minutes. Stir occasionally to keep the onions from sticking.

3. When the carrots are tender, add the sautéed onions and ginger, orange juice, lime juice and cashews. Cook for 5 more minutes to blend the flavors. Let the soup cool slightly.

4. Carefully purée the soup in batches in a blender until very smooth, adding a bit more liquid as needed to make the soup the thickness you want. It should have a velvety texture.

5. Taste the soup and adjust the seasoning as needed, adding more sea salt and/or lime juice. Garnish with chopped cilantro and serve.

Makes 8 – 10 cups

Cauliflower Potato Soup with Dill

You'll never miss the cream in this flavorful and richly satisfying Winter soup.

1 tablespoon olive oil

1½ – 2 cups onion, diced

2 cloves garlic, minced

1 small head cauliflower, cored and chopped (about 3 – 4 cups)

½ cup chopped carrots (scrubbed or peeled)

1 medium potato, diced, 1 – 1½ cups

1½ teaspoon sea salt

¼ teaspoon pepper

2 – 4 tablespoons fresh dill, chopped,
   or 1 tablespoon dried dill weed

½ teaspoon ground mustard seed

4 cups Immune Broth, Chicken Bone Broth,
   or vegetable or chicken stock, or water

1. Heat the olive oil in a medium saucepan. Add the onions and sauté for about 5 minutes until the onions are translucent. Add the garlic and cook for another minute.

2. Add the cauliflower, carrots, potatoes, sea salt, pepper, dill, mustard and stock or water. Bring everything to a boil, reduce the heat to low, and simmer for about 20 minutes, or until the vegetables are very tender.

3. Let the soup cool briefly, then purée it in batches until very smooth. The texture should be velvety.

4. Return the soup to the saucepan and heat.

Makes about 8 cups

Do Ahead

• You can prepare all the vegetables for this soup up to two days ahead of time. Wash and chop them, cover the potatoes in cold water, and store everything in your refrigerator.

• You can cook this soup in the morning, then turn it off, cover it, and let it cool for a few hours before puréeing.

Variations

The proportion of cauliflower, carrot and potatoes is very flexible in this recipe. You can leave out the carrot completely, or decrease the cauliflower and increase the potatoes depending on what you have on hand and how much you love cauliflower!

Tip

Be careful when blending hot soup. Start blending on the lowest setting, increase the speed slowly, and don't fill the blender more than halfway. Hot food will expand under the pressure of the blender.

Golden Pear Soup

This simple soup yields an elegant, subtly sweet flavor that you won't be able to stop eating.

1½ pounds sweet potatoes, yams or butternut squash, peeled and chopped

4 cups water or light vegetable stock

3" cinnamon stick

1¼ teaspoon sea salt

3 large pears, peeled, cored and sliced thin

2 tablespoons butter or olive oil

⅓ cup dry white wine

⅓ – ½ cup dairy or non-dairy milk

1. Place the sweet potatoes, water or stock, cinnamon stick and sea salt in a large pot. Bring to a boil, reduce the heat to low, and simmer, covered, until the sweet potatoes are tender, about 15 minutes. Remove the cinnamon stick.

2. While the sweet potatoes are simmering, melt the butter or olive oil in a large skillet or pot. Add the pears and sauté for 5 to 10 minutes. Add the wine, cover, and simmer for about 15 minutes more, or until the pears are very tender.

3. Add the pears to the sweet potatoes, then stir in the milk.

4. Cool the soup slightly, and then purée in batches until velvety smooth.

5. Return the soup to the pot, taste and adjust the seasonings as needed.

Makes about 8 cups

Do Ahead

• The sweet potatoes can be peeled and chopped up to two days ahead of time.

• You can cook off the sweet potatoes and then refrigerate them up to a day ahead of time.

• You can prepare and cook off the pears up to a day ahead of time.

pear

Pumpkin Curry Soup

½ tablespoon olive oil to sauté

1 cup chopped onion

1 15-ounce can coconut milk

2 cups cooked and mashed yam, winter squash or pumpkin,
  or 1 15-ounce can pumpkin or winter squash

2 cups Immune Broth, Chicken Bone Broth,
  or vegetable or chicken stock, or water

1 – 1½ teaspoons yellow curry paste

1 teaspoon sea salt

2 tablespoons lime juice

½ – 1 tablespoon maple syrup

¼ cup cilantro, chopped

1. In a medium sized soup pot, sauté the onion in the olive oil until tender and translucent, about 5 minutes, stirring every so often.
2. Add the coconut milk, pumpkin, water, curry paste and sea salt, beginning with the smaller amount of curry paste. Bring the soup to a simmer and cook, slightly covered, for about 15 minutes to blend the flavors.
3. Blend the soup using an immersion blender, or carefully blend it in a blender.
4. Add the maple syrup and lime juice, and whisk to combine.
5. Now taste the soup. Add more curry paste (if you want more heat), maple syrup (if you want more sweet) or lime juice (if you want more zing).
6. Stir in the cilantro and serve.

Makes 5½ – 6 cups

Do Ahead

This soup doesn't have much prep, but you can chop the onions and cilantro a day ahead of time.

Tip

Be careful when blending hot soup. Start blending on the lowest setting, increase the speed slowly, and don't fill the blender more than halfway. Hot food will expand under the pressure of the blender.

Do Ahead

You can prepare the onions, ginger, beets and yams up to two days ahead of time.

Variations

If you don't like beets, or don't have any on hand, substitute three cups of washed, stemmed and chopped greens for the beets. You can use kale, collards, mustard greens, chard – whatever is available.

About Ginger

Ginger is perhaps the most life supporting of the spices and has been used for over two thousand years. Not only incredibly delicious, ginger is both antioxidant and antibacterial. Ginger is helpful in treating colds and flu, sore throats, inflammation, nausea, migraines, digestive problems, circulation and arthritis.

Lentil Soup with Beets & Coconut Milk

This gorgeous fuschia soup has a delicate flavor. Packed with nutrition, the spices aid digestion.

1½ cups French green lentils

5 cups Immune Broth, Chicken Bone Broth,
 or vegetable or chicken stock, or water

4" piece kombu seaweed

1 small sweet potato or yam, peeled and diced

1 medium beet, shredded

1 can coconut milk

1 tablespoon olive oil

½ cup minced onions or leeks

1 tablespoon fresh ginger, minced or grated

1 tablespoon ground coriander

1 tablespoon ground fennel seeds

1 teaspoon ground cumin

½ teaspoon ground turmeric

1 teaspoon sea salt

3 – 4 tablespoons fresh cilantro, chopped

1. Rinse the lentils and place them in a saucepan with the kombu and water. Bring to a boil, reduce the heat, and simmer until the lentils are tender, about 15 to 20 minutes.
2. Add the yam, beets and coconut milk and continue simmering, stirring occasionally, until the beets and yams are tender, about 5 minutes.
3. While the lentils are cooking, sauté the onion and ginger until the onion is translucent and tender. Add the spices and sea salt and cook over low heat, stirring, for 3 more minutes.
4. Add the onion mixture to the lentils and continue to simmer for 5 to 10 minutes. Taste and add sea salt as needed.
5. Garnish the soup with chopped cilantro and serve.

Makes 2 – 2½ quarts

Miso Soup with Sea Vegetables, Shiitake Mushrooms & Greens

6 large dried shiitake mushrooms, soaked in 4 cups hot water or broth for 30 minutes (save the water)

¼ ounce arame sea vegetable, soaked in hot water for 10 minutes, then drained

2 cups kale, collard or mustard greens, stemmed and chopped

2 tablespoons miso paste

1 teaspoon minced garlic and/or 1 teaspoon minced ginger (optional)

1 – 2 teaspoons tamari

1 teaspoon umeboshi plum paste

1 or 2 green onions, very thinly sliced

1 or 2 teaspoons toasted sesame seeds

1. Drain the mushrooms and reserve the soaking water. Slice them thinly, discarding the stems.
2. Bring the mushroom soaking water (minus any debris or dirt – strain through cheesecloth or a fine mesh sieve) to a boil in a medium saucepan. Add the sliced shiitakes and the chopped kale.
3. Reduce the heat and simmer for 3 to 5 minutes until the kale is bright green.
4. Remove the soup from the heat and stir in the arame, miso, garlic and/or ginger, tamari and the umeboshi paste. Taste and adjust the seasonings.
5. Garnish the soup with a sprinkling of sliced green onions and toasted sesame seeds.

Makes about 4 cups

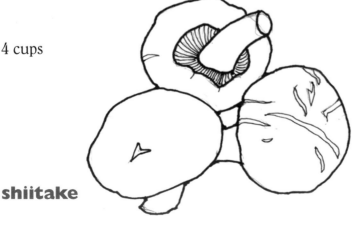

shiitake

Do Ahead

- Soak the shiitakes, then drain, reserving the soaking water. Refrigerate both the mushrooms and water for up to two days.
- Prepare the kale and green onions up to two days ahead of time.

Tips

- This soup is very alkalinizing and we recommend it whenever you are feeling a bit under the weather.
- If dried shiitakes are not available, replace them with a cup of fresh shiitakes, stemmed, sliced and sautéed. Use 4 cups Immune Broth or Chicken Bone Broth, or vegetable or chicken broth instead of the mushroom soaking water.

About Miso

Miso is a fermented soy food that has been eaten in Japan and China for many centuries. While it was once thought that soy was the reason for the low rates of heart disease, breast and prostate cancer in these countries, recent evidence indicates that it is the consumption of traditional fermented soy products (usually eaten every day) that are providing the real benefits.

Fermented foods like miso, tempeh, yogurt, kefir, and sauerkraut help build a healthy ecosystem in the digestive tract. This in turn supports your ability to absorb nutrients from the food you eat, as well as boosting your immunity. Other benefits of miso include:

- Miso is alkalizing and strengthening to the immune system.
- High in antioxidants, miso protects from free radicals that cause signs of aging and other health problems.

Do Ahead

- Steps 1 and 2 can be done up to a day ahead of time.

- The onions, ginger, carrots, bok choy and scallions can be prepared up to two days ahead of time.

Tip

If you reheat this soup, do so very gently. If the soup comes to a simmer, the beneficial enzymes in the miso will be destroyed. Alternately, omit the miso, adding miso to taste to each portion as you eat the soup.

- Miso helps maintain nutritional balance providing protein, vitamins B_{12}, B_2, E, and K, tryptophan, choline, dietary fiber, linoleic acid and lecithin.

- Miso helps reduce the risk of breast, prostate, lung, and colon cancers.

- Miso protects the body against radiation.

Be sure to choose *unpasteurized* miso which has been aged for at least 6 months in order to get the most benefit, and once you add miso to a dish, do not let it come to a boil as this will destroy the healthy bacteria.

The simplest miso soup can be made by heating a cup of Immune Broth or Chicken Bone Broth and whisking in up to a tablespoon of miso.

Miso Ginger Soup with Soba Noodles

4 ounces soba (buckwheat) noodles

8 cups Immune Broth, Chicken Bone Broth, or vegetable or chicken stock, or water

3 or 4 dried shiitake mushrooms or 1 cup of fresh shiitakes, stemmed and sliced

4" piece kombu seaweed

1 tablespoon extra virgin olive oil

1 teaspoon sesame oil

1 onion, peeled and thinly sliced

2 carrots, peeled, cut in half lengthwise and then sliced thinly on the diagonal

2 tablespoons minced fresh ginger

1 small head bok choy or a small bunch mustard or collard greens, thinly sliced

2 tablespoons mirin

¼ cup miso

1 bunch scallions, trimmed and sliced thinly on the diagonal

2 tablespoons lemon juice

1. Put broth or water in a large pot with the shiitake mushrooms and the kombu. Bring everything to a boil. Simmer for five minutes, then add the soba noodles and cook until the soba is tender.

2. Put a colander inside a large bowl. Pour the soup into the colander, saving the stock in the bowl. Return the stock to your pot. Rinse the noodles under cold water and set aside. Thinly slice the shiitakes and set aside.

3. In a large skillet, heat the olive and sesame oil over medium heat. Add the onions and sauté until they are tender and golden, 15 to 20 minutes. Add the carrots and ginger and cook for about five more minutes. Add the mirin to the skillet and cook for a minute or two.

4. Bring your broth back to a boil. Add the onion and carrot mixture along with the greens and the sliced shiitakes. Cook for about five minutes until everything is tender. Turn off the heat.

5. In a small bowl, combine the miso with about ½ cup of the warm broth, whisking to make a smooth mixture. Add the miso to the soup and stir to combine well. Let the soup cool for about 15 minutes, then add the noodles, scallions and the lemon juice to taste.

Makes about 2 quarts

Black Bean Chili with Butternut & Greens

Do Ahead

- Cook the beans up to a day ahead of time, then cool, drain and refrigerate.

- Prepare the onions, butternut and greens up to two days ahead of time: wash the vegetables, chop as instructed, and store in the refrigerator.

2 cups dried black beans, picked over and then soaked overnight, or 3 14-ounce cans black beans, drained and rinsed well

2 quarts water (if cooking black beans)

4" piece Kombu seaweed

1 teaspoon sea salt

2 tablespoons olive oil

2½ cups chopped onions

1 tablespoon minced fresh garlic

1 small butternut or delicata squash, peeled and diced ½", 2 – 3 cups

2 tablespoons chili powder

2 teaspoons ground cumin

2½ cups Immune Broth, Chicken Bone Broth, or vegetable or chicken stock, or water

1 14-ounce can diced tomatoes or 1½ – 2 cups fresh tomatoes, seeded and diced

1 bunch chard, kale or other greens, stems removed, washed well and chopped

¼ – ½ cup fresh cilantro, chopped

1. Drain the dried black beans, place in a medium to large saucepan and cover with 2 quarts of fresh water, kombu and 1 teaspoon sea salt. Bring to a boil, reduce the heat to low, partially cover and cook until the beans are tender, 30 to 45 minutes. (Bean cooking times can vary widely depending on how fresh the beans are. Check at 30 minutes and then every 5 minutes or so until the beans are completely cooked through and very tender.

2. In another large saucepan, heat the olive oil and then add the onions. Sauté, stirring occasionally, until the onions are golden, about 8 minutes.

3. Add the diced winter squash and the garlic and sauté for a couple minutes. Stir in the chili powder and cumin and sauté for 30 seconds.

4. When your beans are tender, drain, reserving the bean cooking water if you want to use it in your chili.

Black Bean Chili

5. Add the beans, 2½ cups of the bean cooking liquid, broth, stock or water, and the diced canned tomatoes to the onion mixture. Bring everything to a boil, reduce the heat to a simmer, and cook uncovered until the squash is tender, about 15 minutes.

6. Stir in the greens and cook for about 5 minutes or until the greens are tender.

7. Season to taste with sea salt and pepper. If desired, stir in cilantro. If you like your chili spicier, add a bit of puréed chipotle chilies to taste or a dash of cayenne pepper.

Makes about 2½ quarts

Tip

Winter Squash can be hard to cut. To make things easier, preheat your oven to 400° and bake the squash until you can pierce it with a fork but it is not yet totally soft. Let the squash cool, then peel, seed and dice.

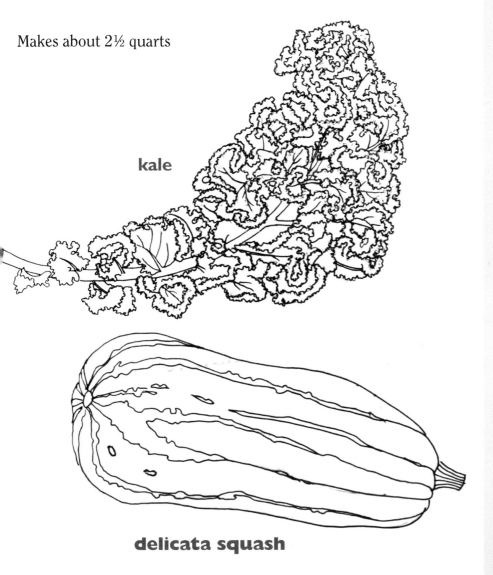

kale

delicata squash

Indian Split Pea Soup with Kale

2 cups split peas, rinsed and picked over

2 quarts Immune Broth, Chicken Bone Broth,
    or vegetable or chicken stock, or water

4" piece kombu seaweed

1 tablespoon olive oil

2 cups chopped onion

1½ cups carrots, peeled or scrubbed, and sliced
    or cut into chunks

1 bunch kale, stems removed and leaves chopped, rinsed well

2 tablespoons minced fresh ginger

1½ tablespoons minced garlic

1½ teaspoons sea salt

1 teaspoon turmeric

½ teaspoon ground cumin

½ teaspoon ground coriander

1. Combine the peas, kombu and water in a large pot and bring to a boil. Reduce the heat to low and simmer, covered, until the peas begin to break apart, about 40 minutes to an hour. Skim off and discard any foam that appears as the peas cook.

2. While the peas are simmering, sauté the onion in the olive oil until it is translucent, about 5 minutes. Add the ginger, garlic, carrots, sea salt and spices, and continue to sauté, stirring often, another 5 minutes or so.

3. Once the peas begin to break apart, add the onion and carrot mixture along with the chopped kale.

4. Continue to simmer the soup until the peas and vegetables are tender, about 20 more minutes.

5. Taste the soup and adjust the seasonings as needed.

Makes about 8 cups

Do Ahead

- The carrots, onion, ginger and kale can all be washed and chopped up to two days ahead of time.

- Up to a day ahead you can complete step 2, sautéing the vegetables and spices together. Refrigerate if you are not making the soup within a couple of hours.

- The peas can be cooked in the morning until they are almost tender, then turned off and covered until later in the day.

Tips

- Once the peas are tender, remove the kombu. If you like, mince it finely and return it to the soup.

- Use your food processor to chop the onions and slice the carrots.

Lima Bean & Turkey Soup

Do Ahead

- All the vegetables for this soup can be prepared up to two days in advance.

- Cook the beans and turkey, then remove the turkey and refrigerate both until you are ready to continue with the soup. Gently reheat the beans, add the turkey meat and vegetables and continue.

1 pound dried large lima beans, soaked overnight

4" piece kombu seaweed

1 turkey drumstick, or 4 – 8 ounces of diced cooked turkey

2 quarts Immune Broth, Chicken Bone Broth, or vegetable or chicken stock, or water

1 onion, peeled and diced

4 stalks celery, diced

4 carrots, peeled and diced

1 14-ounce can diced tomatoes

1 tablespoon minced garlic

2 tablespoons olive oil

2 tablespoons whole wheat, rice or other gluten-free flour

⅛ teaspoon paprika

1 teaspoon dried marjoram

½ teaspoon dried thyme

Sea salt and pepper to taste

1. Drain the beans and place them in a large pot. Add 2 quarts of broth or water, the kombu and the turkey drumstick, if using. Bring to a boil, reduce the heat to low, cover and simmer for 1 to 1½ hours, or until the beans are tender.

2. Remove the meat from the pot and let it cool slightly. Pull the meat off the bones and dice roughly. Discard the bones and excess fat.

3. Return the meat to the pot (or add the diced turkey) along with the carrots, celery, onions and tomatoes. Cover and continue to simmer until the vegetables are tender, about 30 minutes.

4. While the vegetables are cooking, heat the oil and garlic in a small saucepan just until the garlic starts to sizzle, about two minutes. Whisk in the flour and the spices. Cook about two minutes, stirring constantly and being careful not to allow the mixture to get too brown. Whisk in about 1 cup of broth from the soup and cook, whisking constantly, until the mixture is smooth and thickened, another couple of minutes.

5. Stir the flour mixture into the soup and simmer for another ten minutes. Taste and adjust the seasonings.

Makes about 4 quarts and freezes well

Split Mung Dahl

1 tablespoon coconut oil or ghee

1 large onion, minced, about 2 cups

2 tablespoons fresh garlic, minced, about 6 – 7 cloves

1 jalapeño chili, minced (optional)

1 – 2 tablespoons fresh ginger, minced

2 teaspoons turmeric powder

1¾ cups split, washed mung beans

2 zucchini, chopped

1 cup tomatoes, diced or 1 8-ounce can diced tomatoes, drained

7 – 8 cups Immune Broth, Chicken Bone Broth,
    or vegetable or chicken stock, or water

2 teaspoons coconut oil

2 teaspoons black mustard seeds

2 teaspoons cumin seeds

2 teaspoons coriander seeds

½ small bunch of cilantro, chopped

1. Heat the coconut oil in a large heavy-bottom pot. Add the onions and sauté for 15 to 20 minutes until they are caramelized and almost paste-like (this is important as it creates a nice sauce). Add the garlic, ginger, jalapenos (if you are using them), and turmeric. Continue to cook for a few more minutes, adding a bit of oil or water as needed to prevent sticking.

2. Rinse the beans and add them to the pot along with the zucchini. Cook, stirring often, for another 5 minutes.

3. Add the broth or water and the tomatoes, bring to a boil, then reduce the heat to a simmer and cook, covered, for about 1 hour, until the beans are soft.

4. Heat the remaining coconut oil over medium heat in a small skillet. Add the mustard, cumin and coriander seeds and cook until they are fragrant and beginning to pop, being careful not to burn them. Add the spices to the dahl along with the chopped cilantro.

Makes about 2½ quarts

Do Ahead

All of the vegetables can be prepared up to a day ahead of time.

About Mung Beans

Mung beans are one of the most cherished foods in the Indian ayurvedic system of healing because they are balancing to all constitutional types. They are nourishing and don't often cause the gas or bloating experienced with other beans.

Mushroom Barley Soup

½ cup barley, soaked overnight

4" piece kombu seaweed

½ tablespoon olive oil

1½ cups chopped onion

2 teaspoons garlic, minced

2 carrots, peeled or scrubbed and diced

2 stalks celery, diced

½ teaspoon sea salt

¼ teaspoon pepper

¼ teaspoon dried thyme

6 cups Immune Broth, Chicken Bone Broth, or vegetable or chicken stock, or water

1 tablespoon tamari

1 tablespoons olive oil

¼ pound shiitake, maitake or trumpet royale mushrooms, stemmed and sliced

½ pound white or cremini mushrooms, stemmed and sliced

4 ounces cooked turkey or chicken, diced (optional)

2 – 4 tablespoons chopped fresh parsley

1. Place the barley and kombu in a small saucepan with 3 to 4 cups of water. Bring it to a boil, reduce the heat to a simmer and cook until the barley is tender, about 20 minutes. Drain, rinse and set aside.

2. In a soup pot, sauté the onion in the olive oil until it's translucent, 5 to 10 minutes. Add the garlic, carrots, celery, sea salt and thyme and sauté for another five minutes until the vegetables are beginning to be tender.

3. Add the broth or water and the tamari and bring the soup to a boil, reduce the heat, and simmer, partially covered.

4. Heat 2 tablespoons of olive oil in a large skillet over high heat. When the pan is hot, add the mushrooms and cook, stirring every minute or so, until they are tender and beginning to brown. Add them to the soup.

5. Add the barley and the optional chicken or turkey and simmer the soup for 15 to 20 minutes to blend the flavors. Taste and adjust the seasonings. Stir in parsley and serve.

Makes about 2½ quarts

Winter Minestrone with Barley

1 cup pearl barley

4" piece kombu

1 can white beans, drained and rinsed or ½ cup dry beans,
  soaked overnight and then cooked until tender

1 can kidney beans, drained and rinsed or ½ cup dry beans,
  soaked overnight and then cooked until tender

1 tablespoons olive oil

1 onion, chopped

2 carrots, peeled and roughly chopped

2 stalks celery, roughly chopped

1 fennel bulb, trimmed, cored and chopped

1 tablespoon garlic, minced

1 tablespoon each: chopped sage, rosemary and thyme,
  or 1 teaspoon of each, dried

1 teaspoon sea salt

4 – 6 cups Immune Broth, Chicken Bone Broth,
  or vegetable or chicken stock, or water

1 28-ounce can diced tomatoes with their juice,
  or 3 cups fresh tomatoes, chopped

½ small head cabbage, shredded, about 3 cups

½ cup chopped parsley

Do Ahead

- The onion, celery, carrots, fennel and cabbage can be prepared up to two days ahead of time. Package the onion and cabbage separately. The celery, carrots and fennel can be packaged together.

- The barley can be cooked a day ahead of time. Drain, rinse and refrigerate.

1. Bring 1 quart water to a boil, add the barley and kombu, cover, reduce the heat to low, and cook for about 20 minutes. Drain and set aside.

2. Warm the olive oil in a large pot and add the chopped onion. Cook over medium low heat for 5 to 10 minutes or until the onion is translucent. Add the carrots, celery, fennel and garlic, and continue sautéing for five minutes. Add the fresh or dried herbs and the sea salt and sauté for another 30 seconds.

3. Add the broth or water, tomatoes, cabbage, barley and the drained beans. Bring to a boil, stirring occasionally, and simmer for about 20 minutes or until the barley and the vegetables are tender.

4. Taste the soup and add sea salt as needed. Stir in the parsley and serve.

Makes about 3½ quarts and freezes well

Chilled Cucumber Avocado Soup

3 cups cucumbers, peeled, seeded and sliced or roughly chopped

2 ripe avocados, peeled, pits removed

1 tablespoon chopped garlic

½ cup fresh chopped parsley

2 cups yogurt

1½ cups cold water

½ teaspoon sea salt

¼ cup minced fresh scallions (optional)

1. Working in two batches, blend the cucumbers, avocado, garlic, parsley, yogurt, water and sea salt until very smooth. Whisk the soup to combine, then taste and adjust the seasonings.
2. Stir in the minced scallions if desired.
3. Refrigerate the soup until cold.

Makes about 7 – 8 cups

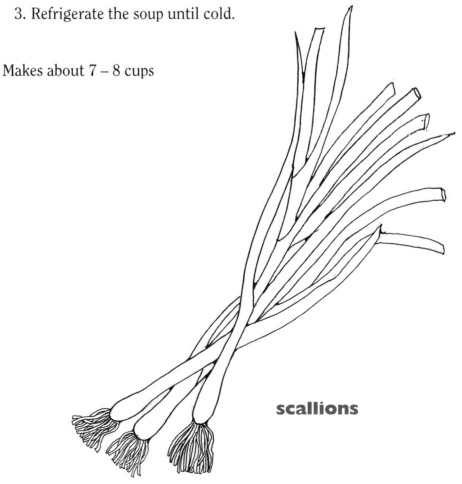

scallions

Tip

To seed cucumbers, cut them in half lengthwise and then use a teaspoon to scrape out the seeds from each half.

Variation

You can also try this with goat yogurt, kefir or non-dairy milk instead of the regular yogurt.

"Cancer is, of course, a challenge – the surgeries, the myriad of medical appointments, the tremendous amount to learn in order to make wise decisions. Through this, the food has come every week – nothing I'd ever have likely prepared, but it has been absolutely delicious and we are just so very grateful."

– Catherine

Chilled Minted Zucchini Soup

1 teaspoon extra virgin olive oil

1½ pounds zucchini (about 5 small), sliced thin

½ teaspoon fresh minced garlic

3 cups water

¾ cup yogurt

¼ cup fresh mint leaves, washed, spun dry and minced

Sea salt and pepper to taste

1. In a medium-sized sauce pan, heat the olive oil over moderately high heat. Add about one-third of the zucchini and sauté, stirring occasionally, until golden. Add the garlic and sauté for another minute or two.
2. Add the rest of the zucchini and the water. Bring to a simmer and cook until the zucchini is very tender, about 15 minutes. Cool.
3. Carefully purée the soup in a blender. Whisk in the yogurt, mint and sea salt and pepper to taste. Taste and adjust the seasonings.
4. Chill, covered, until cold.

Makes 7 – 8 cups

Do Ahead

• The zucchini can be sliced up to two days ahead of time.

• Cook the soup in the morning. Turn it off and let it sit for a couple hours, covered, then purée.

Tip

Use your food processor to slice the zucchini.

I don't know how to fully express what a lifesaver the Ceres Project food was for me during my chemo. Having food already prepared, tasty food which I knew was good for me and helping me fight the cancer, made my life so much easier during an extremely difficult time. Having cancer sucks, but it has made me realize not only how much I am loved by my friends and family, but how loving and supportive this community is.

Malia MacDiarmid

Chapter 6•Dips, Dressings & Sauces

RECIPES

Hummus

Cucumber Yogurt Dip with Dill

1 English cucumber

1 tablespoon coarse sea salt

2 cups plain yogurt or kefir

½ cup sour cream (optional)

2 tablespoons fresh lemon juice

2 tablespoons fresh dill weed, minced

1 teaspoon minced garlic

1. Wash the cucumber, cut in half lengthwise and scoop out the seeds using a small spoon. Grate the cucumber and put it in a bowl with the sea salt. Toss together and then chill for 3 hours in the refrigerator.
2. Whisk together the yogurt, sour cream, lemon juice, dill and minced garlic.
3. Squeeze out as much liquid as you can from the cucumber, then stir it into the yogurt mixture. Taste and adjust seasonings with more dill, garlic or lemon.
4. Refrigerate for an hour or two to blend the flavors.

Makes 3 cups

Do Ahead

You can prepare the recipe through step 1 a day ahead of time.

Variation

You can omit the dill and replace it with chopped fresh mint, cilantro and/or parsley, or add any of those herbs along with the dill.

Tip

Cucumber Yogurt Dip is delicious with raw vegetables or pita wedges. Serve it as a sauce with baked or grilled fish such as salmon or sea bass.

Feta & Sun-dried Tomato Spread with Basil

Tips

Feta & Sun-dried Tomato Spread is so delicious you'll discover a myriad of uses:

- Spread it on some whole grain bread and make a sandwich with sliced turkey, slivered red onion and some lettuce, or with sprouts, cucumber and sliced tomatoes.

- Spread it on sprouted whole wheat pita.

- Use it as a dip for raw vegetables.

- Cut a cucumber in half lengthwise, scoop out the seeds and fill the cavity with the spread or use it to stuff celery stalks or endive leaves.

8 ounces real cream cheese, or Neufchâtel if you want to lower the fat content

½ cup yogurt

⅓ cup sun-dried tomato halves in oil, drained and chopped

3 tablespoons pine nuts, toasted

3 tablespoons fresh basil, chopped

1 clove garlic, minced

6 – 8 ounces feta cheese, crumbled

1. Put the cream cheese, yogurt, sun-dried tomatoes, pine nuts, basil and garlic in the food processor. Process until everything is incorporated and the mixture is smooth.
2. Add the crumbled feta and process just to mix it in. The texture should be a bit lumpy!
3. Put the feta spread in a bowl and chill until ready to serve.

Makes about 3 cups

Green Goddess Dressing or Dip

This easy, delicious dressing is packed with the nutritional goodness of fresh herbs.

1 cup packed watercress, arugula or parsley leaves

¾ cup plain yogurt

⅓ cup mayonnaise

2 tablespoons fresh dill, chopped

2 tablespoons fresh basil, chopped

2 tablespoons scallions, chopped

1 tablespoon fresh mint, chopped (optional)

1 teaspoon red wine vinegar

Sea salt and pepper to taste

1. Put all of the ingredients in a blender and blend until creamy. Taste and adjust the seasonings with more sea salt and pepper, a dash more red wine vinegar or a bit more of any of the herbs.
2. Use as a salad dressing or dip for fresh vegetables. Drizzle over grilled fish. Use as a dressing for pasta salad. Invent your own use!

Makes 1¼ cups

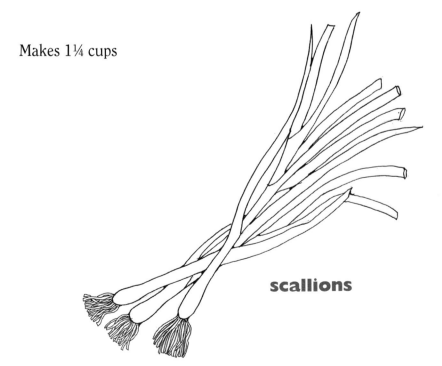

scallions

Variations

- To make this without dairy, omit the yogurt and mayonnaise. In their place, add ¼ cup packed crumbled tofu, ¼ cup olive oil and 2 tablespoons fresh lemon juice. Thin the dressing as needed with a non-dairy milk.

- Feel free to experiment with the proportion of herbs and scallions, or add a small clove of minced garlic.

- You can use buttermilk, sour cream, yogurt and/or mayonnaise for the base in any proportion.

Other Dressings, Sauces & Dips

- Asian Coconut Almond Dressing or Sauce, page 76

- Sesame Tamari Dressing or Marinade, page 87

- Ginger Lime Vinaigrette or Marinade, page 163

- Miso Tahini Sauce or Dressing, page 128

- Basil, Arugula and Cilantro Lime Pestos, page 132

- Sun-dried Tomato & Olive Pesto, page 158

- Vegetarian Burgundy Gravy, page 144

Hummus

1 15-ounce can garbanzo beans, drained and rinsed
⅔ cup raw sesame tahini
⅓ cup lemon juice
2 – 3 cloves garlic, minced
1 tablespoon tamari
½ teaspoon ground cumin

3. Place the drained beans, tahini, lemon juice, garlic, tamari and cumin in a food processor and process until creamy.
4. After the hummus begins to have a smooth texture, add ¼ cup at a time of water, or reserved garbanzo cooking water, until you reach the desired consistency.
5. Taste the hummus and adjust the seasonings – more lemon, garlic, tamari or cumin – to suit your tastes.

Makes about 2½ cups

Variations

Use this basic recipe to experiment with other types of bean dip.

• Use white beans instead of chickpeas.

• Add ½ cup of roasted red pepper to the dip for a rosy glow

• Add ¼ to ½ cup of chopped parsley to add more antioxidants.

• Omit the tahini, add ¼ cup of olive oil and 3 to 4 tablespoons of roasted garlic.

There are as many versions as your creativity will allow!

Tips

• To make this with dried beans, soak about 1½ cups dried beans overnight in four cups of water. Drain, cover with fresh water and ½ teaspoon sea salt, and cook until very tender, 45 minutes to 1½ hours depending on the freshness of your beans. Drain the beans and save the water to use when you are thinning the hummus.

• Use the resulting 3½ or so cups of beans to make a double batch of hummus, then freeze half. Hummus will keep well in your freezer for up to one month.

• Hummus is a great way to get your calcium. Each tablespoon of tahini has 128 grams of this important nutrient.

Chapter 7 • Vegetarian Main Dishes

RECIPES

Filo with Chard, Caramelized Onions & Tofu

Kichadi Plus

¾ cup split mung beans (sprouted if possible)

¾ cup Basmati rice, white or brown

2 teaspoons ghee (clarified unsalted butter) or olive oil

I teaspoon mustard seeds

I ½ teaspoon whole cumin seeds

I teaspoon fennel seeds or ½ teaspoon fenugreek seeds

½ – I teaspoon coriander powder,

I teaspoon turmeric

¼ teaspoon cardamom

I" piece of fresh ginger, grated

2 – 4 cups of washed and chopped vegetables of your choice,
   such as:

• Slow cooking: sweet potato, winter squash, carrot, turnip, lotus
   root, burdock root, kale

• Fast cooking: broccoli, asparagus, summer squash,
   green beans, peas, spinach, chard

7 – 8 cups Immune Broth, Chicken Bone Broth,
   or vegetable or chicken stock, or water

1. Cover the mung beans and rice with water and let it soak for at
   least 30 minutes while you prepare the rest of your ingredients.

2. Heat the ghee or olive oil in a 3 quart saucepan. Add the
   mustard, cumin and fennel seeds. Stir, cooking over medium
   heat, until they begin to pop. Reduce the heat to low and stir in
   the ground herbs and fresh ginger. Cook, stirring continually,
   until you begin to smell their aromas, about 30 to 45 seconds.

3. Add the slow-cooking vegetables to the ghee and spices along
   with the drained rice and mung beans. Stir to coat all the
   ingredients with the spice mixture.

4. Add about 4 cups of broth or water. Bring everything to a boil,
   then cover and reduce the heat to medium low. Cook for 15 to
   20 minutes, then add another 3 to 4 cups of broth or water (if
   you want a soupier Kichadi) and any remaining quick-cooking
   vegetables. Continue cooking until everything is very tender,
   another 10 to 20 minutes.

5. Garnish with any or all of the following: tamari, Bragg's Aminos,
   gomasio, toasted pumpkin seeds, toasted coconut, goji berries, or
   yogurt.

Serves 4

Do Ahead

• You can prepare your vegetables up to a day in advance.

• Soaking the basmati and split mung beans overnight improves their digestibility even more and speeds the cooking process.

Tip

You can make the Kichadi with any amount of water, from 4 to 8 cups, depending on the consistency that you want. More water will make a soupier dish while the smaller amount will result in a consistency more like a pilaf.

About Kichadi

Kichadi (kitchari, kitcharee) is one of the traditional foods used in India's Ayurvedic system of healing. Kitchadi is recommended anytime you are feeling under the weather, need cleansing, or to rest and rejuvenate the deeper tissues. Made with nutritive-rich and easily digested mung beans and basmati rice, the combination offers balanced protein and carbohydrates. The simplicity of the dish along with its healing spices help support digestion. The more liquid you use, the easier it is to digest.

Variation

Instead of mushrooms, toss the marinade with a selection of vegetables. Try summer squash, eggplant, peppers, cauliflower, sweet potatoes and/or winter squash. Roast the vegetables in a 400° oven until they are tender and beginning to caramelize. Serve over the polenta garnished with the cheese.

Herbed Polenta with Grilled Portobello Mushrooms

1 cup polenta

4 cups boiling Immune Broth, Chicken Bone Broth, vegetable or chicken stock, water, or use up to 1 cup dairy or non-dairy milk

1 clove garlic, minced

¼ cup fresh parsley, chopped

1½ teaspoons fresh thyme leaves, minced, or ½ teaspoon dried

1½ teaspoons fresh rosemary, minced, or ½ teaspoon dried

Sea salt and freshly ground black pepper, to taste

¼ cup grated Parmigiana-Reggiano cheese (optional)

4 large Portobello mushrooms, stems removed

3 tablespoons olive oil

1 tablespoon balsamic vinegar

1½ teaspoons mirin

1. Preheat the oven to 350°.
2. In a large, oven-proof pot, bring the water to a boil. Slowly pour in the polenta, whisking continuously. Reduce the heat to low and add the garlic, parsley, rosemary, thyme and sea salt and pepper.
3. Place the pot in the oven and bake, uncovered, for 20 minutes, then stir well. Bake an additional 20 minutes or until the polenta is creamy.
4. While polenta cooks, whisk together the olive oil, balsamic vinegar and mirin. Brush the mushroom caps with the mixture, coating them on both sides. Sprinkle with sea salt and pepper. Grill the portobellos, underside down, on a very hot grill for about 4 minutes. Turn and cook until tender all the way through, an additional 4 minutes. Alternately, place the mushrooms on a baking sheet in a 450° oven and cook until they are tender, about 15 to 20 minutes.
5. Slice the mushrooms into thick, ½" slices. Divide the polenta among four plates and top each serving with a sliced mushroom cap. Sprinkle with the grated cheese and serve immediately.

Serves 4

Miso Tahini Rice with Kale & Carrots

1 cup brown rice, soaked for one hour or overnight

1 large leek, white and pale green parts
 ~ or ~ ½ – 1 yellow or red onion, peeled and chopped

2 carrots, peeled, cut in half lengthwise and sliced on the diagonal

1 bunch kale, chard or collard greens, washed, stemmed and
 roughly chopped

1 – 2 tablespoons olive oil

2 cloves garlic

1 shallot, minced (optional)

1 teaspoon minced garlic

3 tablespoons lemon juice

3 tablespoons white miso

3 tablespoons tahini

¼ cup olive oil

½ cup water

2 tablespoons toasted sesame seeds

1. Drain the rice and place it in a pot with 1½ cups water and
 ¼ teaspoon sea salt. Bring to a boil, cover and reduce the
 heat to low. Cook until the rice is tender and all the water is
 absorbed, 25 to 35 minutes. If the rice becomes dry and is not
 tender, add ¼ cup water, cook for 5 more minutes and check.
 When the rice is done, place it in a large bowl.

2. Heat the olive oil in a large skillet over medium heat. Add the
 leek or onion and cook for 2 to 3 minutes. Add the carrots and
 continue cooking, stirring every few minutes, until the onion is
 beginning to brown and the carrots are almost tender.

3. Add the chopped kale and the garlic, stir to combine everything,
 and then reduce the heat and cover the pot. Stir every few minutes
 and continue to cook until the kale and carrots are tender. Add the
 cooked vegetables to the rice and stir to combine evenly.

4. To make the sauce, combine the shallots, garlic, lemon juice, miso,
 tahini, olive oil and water in a blender and blend until smooth.
 Alternately, whisk the ingredients or use an immersion blender.

5. Toss the rice and vegetable mixture with enough sauce to coat
 everything evenly. Add the toasted sesame seeds and stir to
 combine.

Serves 4 – 6

Do Ahead

- You can prepare all of your vegetables up to two days in advance.

- You can make the sauce up to two days in advance. This sauce also makes a wonderful salad dressing so make a double batch!

- You can cook the rice a day ahead of time.

- You can cook off your vegetables a day ahead of time.

Variations

- Miso Tahini Rice can be served warm as a side dish or cold as a salad. Adding cooked sliced chicken or cubed and sautéed tempeh will increase the protein content.

- Use the Miso Tahini Sauce as a salad dressing or dip for vegetables. Fill a pita half with hummus and salad greens, then drizzle Miso Tahini Sauce over the top.

Tip

If you are using a leek, trim it, quarter it lengthwise, and slice. Then place the chopped leeks in a colander and rinse very well under running water as dirt is often trapped in the leek's layers.

Do Ahead

- All of the vegetables can be prepared up to two days in advance. They can be cooked off the night before or in the morning.

- The rices can be cooked a day in advance or use 4 cups of any leftover grain.

Variation

Any combination of wild and brown rice will work just fine so feel free to use all one or the other, or try making the pilaf with other grains such as barley, millet or quinoa.

Basmati & Wild Rice Pilaf with Mushrooms & Greens

1 cup brown rice, soaked for at least an hour or overnight

½ cup wild rice

3 cups Immune Broth, Chicken Bone Broth, or vegetable or chicken stock, or water

¼ teaspoon sea salt

2 tablespoons olive oil

1 red or yellow onion, minced

3 ribs celery, diced

½ pound cremini, shiitake, or other mushrooms, stemmed and sliced

1 tablespoon fresh rosemary, minced, or ½ teaspoon dried

1 bunch collard greens, kale or chard, washed, stemmed and chopped

½ cup dried cranberries or goji berries

1 tablespoon umeboshi plum vinegar

½ cup arame sea vegetable, soaked for 10 minutes in hot water, then drained

½ cup fresh parsley, chopped

½ cup toasted pecans or walnuts

1. Drain the brown rice and then put it in a medium-sized saucepan with the wild rice, broth, stock or water and sea salt. Bring to a boil, reduce the heat to low, and cook for 30 to 40 minutes or until the rice is tender and the water is absorbed.

2. In a large skillet over medium heat, sauté the onion in olive oil until translucent, about five minutes. Add the celery, mushrooms and rosemary and sauté until the mushrooms are tender, about five more minutes.

3. Add the greens and cranberries or goji berries, cover, and cook for 5 to 10 more minutes or until all of the vegetables are tender. Add the umeboshi plum vinegar and stir to combine.

4. When the rice is tender, place it in a large bowl. Add the vegetable mixture, arame and fresh parsley and toss to combine everything evenly. Garnish with the toasted nuts.

Serves 4 – 6

Quinoa Pilaf with Almonds & Goji Berries

1½ cups quinoa, soaked for at least one hour and preferably overnight

1 – 1¼ cups water

¼ cup goji berries, dried cranberries or raisins

Pinch of sea salt

1 tablespoon olive oil

1 red onion, chopped, about 1½ cups

¼ teaspoon cinnamon

¼ teaspoon ground ginger

¼ teaspoon ground coriander

⅛ teaspoon turmeric

¾ teaspoon ground cumin

6 tablespoons toasted chopped almonds

¼ – ½ cup chopped parsley

1. Drain the quinoa and rinse it well under running water. Put it in a pot with the water, sea salt and goji berries. Bring everything to a boil, cover, reduce the heat to very low, and cook for 8 to 12 minutes, or until the quinoa is soft and the water is absorbed. Turn off the heat and let it sit for 5 to 10 minutes.
2. While the quinoa is cooking, sauté the onion in the olive oil until it is translucent and tender. Add all of the spices and cook for another couple of minutes, stirring often.
3. When the quinoa is tender, add the spiced onion mixture along with the almonds and parsley. Toss to combine well.

Serves 4

Do Ahead

The onion can be chopped a day ahead of time.

Variations

- This pilaf is also wonderful with some cubed and sautéed tempeh or diced cooked chicken.

- Try this same spice mixture tossed with other grains such as brown rice, millet or barley.

- Use the pilaf to stuff baked squash halves. Use acorn, sweet dumpling or delicata squash. Cut the squash in half, seed and bake, cut side down, in a 400° oven until tender. Turn cut side up and stuff with the pilaf.

Do Ahead

All of the vegetables can be prepared up to two days in advance.

"Cooking is not a particularly difficult art, and the more you cook and learn about cooking, the more sense it makes. But like any art, it requires practice and experience. The most important ingredient you can bring to it is love of cooking for its own sake."

– Julia Child

Pasta Fagioli

Quite simple to prepare, this nourishing meal in a pot includes nutrient-rich beans, whole grain pasta and dark leafy greens.

1 tablespoon olive oil

1 yellow onion, chopped, about 1½ – 2 cups

4 cloves garlic, minced

3 ribs celery, chopped into ½-inch pieces

1½ teaspoon Italian seasoning
   or a mixture of dried basil and oregano

¼ teaspoon crushed red pepper flakes (optional)

Sea salt to taste

2 cups Immune Broth, Chicken Bone Broth,
   or vegetable or chicken stock, or water

1 14-ounce can crushed tomatoes or
   1½ – 2 cups fresh tomatoes, seeded and diced

1 cup uncooked whole-wheat, quinoa
   or kamut pasta, rotini or small shells

1 cup fresh spinach or chard, chopped, packed

1 15-ounce can cannellini beans or kidney beans, drained and
   rinsed, or ½ cup dry beans, soaked overnight and then
   cooked until tender

¼ cup chopped fresh parsley

2 tablespoons grated Parmesan cheese (optional)

1. Heat the oil in a large saucepan over medium heat. Add the onion, garlic, celery, herbs and red pepper flakes if you are using them. Sauté, stirring often, until the onions are tender.
2. Add the broth and tomatoes, reduce the heat to low and simmer for about 20 minutes.
3. Add the pasta and cook until tender, about 10 to 15 minutes.
4. Add the spinach or chard, beans and parsley. Stir gently for a few minutes until the greens have wilted and the mixture is heated through. Serve with grated cheese on top.

Serves 4 – 6

Kamut Pasta with Vegetables & Pesto

Do Ahead

- The pesto can be made up to two days ahead of time.
- The vegetables can be prepared up to two days ahead of time.
- The vegetables can be cooked up to a day ahead of time.

"Eat food as close to nature as possible, eat what's in season, prepare it simply, chew slowly, and give thanks."

– Rosemary Gradstar

Basic Basil Pesto

4 cups loosely packed basil leaves

½ cup pine nuts, toasted

2 teaspoons minced garlic

¼ teaspoon sea salt

½ cup olive oil

¼ cup grated Parmesan, Romano or Asiago cheese (optional)

Zesty Spring Pesto with Arugula

4 cups loosely packed arugula leaves

½ cup pine nuts or walnuts, toasted

2 teaspoons minced garlic

¼ teaspoon sea salt

½ cup olive oil

¼ cup grated Parmesan, Romano or Asiago cheese (optional)

Cilantro Pesto with Ginger & Cashews

4 cups fresh cilantro (2 large bunches, most of stems cut off)

I cup cashews

⅓ cup lime juice

2 tablespoons toasted sesame oil

⅓ cup olive oil

I tablespoon minced garlic

4 teaspoons minced ginger

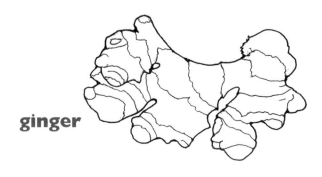

ginger

Kamut Pasta

Pesto

1. Decide which pesto you want to make, then combine all the ingredients in a food processor and process until the pesto is smooth and evenly combined.
2. Taste and adjust with more garlic, ginger, sea salt or lime depending on which one you are making and your own taste buds.

Pasta

12 ounces kamut or other whole-grain pasta

4 – 6 cups of assorted vegetables: asparagus, sugar snap peas, fresh shelling peas, baby carrots, broccoli, cauliflower, summer squash, peppers

Shredded Asiago cheese for garnish

1. Prepare each of your vegetables and cut into interesting shapes – asparagus on the diagonal, broccoli and cauliflower in florets, snow peas or sugar snaps left whole, carrots cut in half lengthwise and then sliced on the diagonal.
2. Bring a medium-sized pot of water to a boil. Blanch each of the vegetables one at a time until they are tender but still brightly colored. Immediately cool under running water to set the color. Repeat until all of your vegetables are cooked.
3. While you are blanching the vegetables, bring a large pot of salted water to a boil. Cook the pasta just until al dente, following the package directions. Drain, rinse well under hot water, and then drain again.
4. Put the pasta in a large bowl and toss it with the pesto you've chosen. Add your vegetables and toss again to combine everything evenly.
5. Serve garnished with toasted nuts and a bit of grated cheese if desired.

Serves 4 – 6

Variations

- This dish is equally good eaten at room temperature as a pasta salad. Feel free to add minced red onion, halved cherry tomatoes, thinly sliced celery or other raw vegetables as well as the cooked ones suggested here.

- You can make this dish with any assortment of vegetables that you have on hand, either blanched, roasted or sautéed.

- In the winter, toss the pasta with the Sun-dried Tomato Pesto on page xx.

Other uses for Pesto

- Use as a sandwich spread.

- Spread on raw chicken or fish fillets and bake.

- Toss with cooked grains.

- Toss with roasted or steamed vegetables.

Pasta with Chard, Winter Squash & Caramelized Onions

2 tablespoons olive oil

2 medium onions, cut in half and then thinly sliced

1 tablespoon minced garlic

4 cups peeled and diced delicata or butternut squash

2 bunches chard, stems removed, washed and chopped, or use kale or collard greens

¼ cup sundried tomatoes in oil, chopped (optional)

½ cup chopped parsley

12 ounces kamut or other whole grain pasta

½ cup crumbled Gorgonzola cheese, blue cheese or feta, or grated fresh Parmesan cheese (optional)

1. Heat the olive oil over medium heat in a large skillet. Add the onions and cook, stirring often, until they are tender and turn a golden brown, 15 to 20 minutes.
2. Add the garlic and the diced winter squash, cover the pan and reduce the heat slightly. Cook for about 5 minutes.
3. Add the chard and sun-dried tomatoes to the pot and continue to cook, covered, until all of the vegetables are tender. This will take about 10 more minutes. If things begin to stick, add ¼ cup of water to the pan.
4. While the vegetables are cooking, bring a large pot of sea salted water to a boil. Cook the pasta according to the package directions, just until it is al dente. Drain, rinse under hot water and return it to the pot.
5. When the vegetables are tender, toss them with the pasta along with the chopped fresh parsley. Garnish with cheese if desired.

Serves 4 – 6

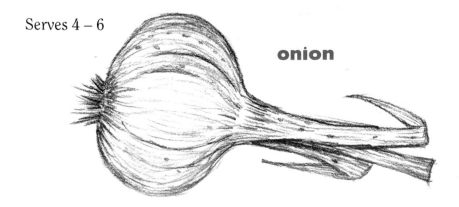

onion

Do Ahead

- All of the vegetables can be prepared up to two days in advance.

- The vegetables can be cooked the night before or in the morning.

- The pasta can be cooked the night before or in the morning.

Variation

This pasta is excellent with the addition of some cooked, sliced chicken sausage, cubed cooked chicken or tempeh.

Easy Vegetable Lasagna

Do Ahead

- The vegetables can be prepared up to two days ahead of time and sautéed up to a day ahead of time.

- The ricotta mixture can be assembled up to a day ahead of time.

- The cheese can be grated up to 2 days ahead of time.

- The lasagna can be assembled the night before or in the morning. Cover tightly and store in the refrigerator. Let the lasagna sit at room temperature for an hour before baking or add about 15 minutes to your baking time.

1 pound lasagna noodles, preferably whole grain or rice

4 cups part-skim ricotta cheese

1 large egg

¼ cup Parmesan cheese

1 teaspoon sea salt

1 teaspoon black pepper

2 10-ounce packages chopped frozen spinach, thawed and drained well, or 4 bunches fresh spinach, cleaned, cooked just to wilt and then pressed to remove water

2 tablespoons olive oil

1 small yellow onion, finely chopped, about 1½ cups

2 tablespoons minced garlic

1 zucchini, chopped

2 red, yellow or orange bell peppers, seeded and diced

½ teaspoon sea salt

½ teaspoon oregano

8 ounces mozzarella cheese, grated

2 24-ounce jars organic pasta sauce, any flavor, or about 6 cups homemade sauce

1. Bring a large pot of salted water to a boil. Add the lasagna noodles and cook, stirring a couple of times in the beginning to make sure the noodles don't stick together. When the noodles are just al dente (check the package directions), drain and gently rinse in cold water. Separate the noodles and set aside.

2. Blend together the ricotta, egg, Parmesan, sea salt and pepper. Add half the spinach and mix to combine everything evenly. Set aside.

Easy Vegetable Lasagna

3. Heat the olive oil over medium heat in a large skillet. Add the onion and sauté until it is just translucent. Add the garlic, zucchini and peppers and continue to cook until all the vegetables are tender. Add the sea salt, oregano and the rest of the spinach and cook for 1 to 2 more minutes to blend the flavors. Set aside.

4. Preheat the oven to 375° and grease a 9" x 13" pan.

5. Now you are ready to assemble the lasagna. Make layers as follows:

   - 1½ cups of sauce
   - A layer of noodles
   - All of the vegetable sauté
   - ½ of the ricotta and spinach mixture
   - ½ of the mozzarella
   - 2 cups of sauce
   - A layer of noodles
   - The rest of the ricotta mixture
   - The rest of the mozzarella
   - A layer of noodles
   - 2 cups of sauce
   - Some grated Parmesan cheese

6. Bake for 40 to 50 minutes until the lasagna is golden brown and bubbling around the edges. Let sit for 15 to 20 minutes before serving.

Serves 6 – 9

Variations

- To make a non-dairy version of this lasagna, substitute the tofu filling mixture on page 142 for the ricotta, egg, Parmesan cheese and sea salt and pepper.

- You can use two large bunches of chard instead of the frozen spinach. Remove the stems, steam until tender, then rinse under cold water, drain well, and chop finely.

- Feel free to use whatever mixture of chopped and sautéed vegetables that you want. Mushrooms, broccoli, green beans, asparagus and artichoke hearts make great additions.

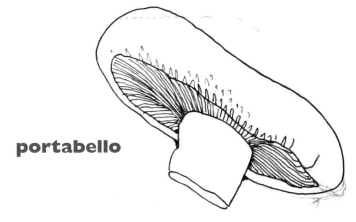

portabello

Asian Noodle Stir Fry with Arame & Broccoli

8 ounces Asian rice noodles* (not rice pasta)

1 pound broccoli, florets and peeled, sliced stems, about 5 – 6 cups

½ cup arame sea vegetable

½ pound trumpet royale, shiitake or other mushrooms, stemmed and thinly sliced

1 red or yellow bell pepper, seeded and cut in strips

1 tablespoon regular (not toasted) sesame oil

2 teaspoons minced garlic

1 tablespoon fresh ginger, minced

½ cup chopped scallions

1 tablespoon tamari

3 tablespoons tamari

3 tablespoons fresh lime juice

1 tablespoon toasted sesame oil

Toasted sesame seeds for garnish

1. Cook the noodles in plenty of boiling salted water for 3 to 4 minutes or just until tender. Rice noodles cook quickly so watch them carefully. Drain and rinse well under cold water. Drain again and transfer to a large bowl. Toss with sesame oil to prevent the noodles from sticking.

2. Blanch the broccoli just until tender and bright green. Rinse under cold water to stop the cooking. Set aside.

3. Cover the arame in hot water. Set aside for 10 minutes, then drain well and toss with the noodles.

4. Heat the sesame oil in a large skillet over medium heat. Add the mushrooms and peppers and sauté until almost tender, stirring often.

5. Add the ginger, garlic and scallions and sauté for 2 to 3 minutes. Add 1 tablespoon of tamari and the cooked broccoli and sauté for one more minute to re-warm the broccoli.

6. Whisk together the remaining tamari, lime juice and toasted sesame oil. Taste and adjust the seasonings. Toss the dressing with the noodles.

7. Serve the noodles topped with the vegetable mixture and garnish with toasted sesame seeds.

Serves 4 – 6

Do Ahead

- All of the vegetables can be prepared up to two days ahead of time.

- The dressing can be prepared up to two days ahead of time.

- You can sauté the vegetables and soak the arame up to a day ahead of time. Drain the arame after 10 minutes or so.

- The noodles can be cooked in the morning. Toss with the sesame oil to prevent sticking. If the noodles do stick, run them under cold water, then drain before adding the dressing.

Variations

- This basic stir fry can be made with any combination of vegetables that you have on hand. Use carrots, zucchini, green beans, sugar snap or snow peas, bok choy or napa cabbage.

- Instead of rice noodles, serve the stir fry over steamed brown rice or another cooked grain.

* You can find Asian rice noodles in the Asian section of most grocery stores or at an Asian market.

Do Ahead

- The soba noodles can be cooked a day ahead of time. Toss them with a teaspoon or so of olive oil to prevent them from sticking.

- The vegetables can be prepared up to two days ahead of time.

Kale & Shiitake Stir Fry with Soba Noodles

8 ounces soba (buckwheat) noodles

1 bunch kale, any variety, stems removed

3 tablespoons olive oil

1 medium yellow or red onion onion, peeled, cut in half and thinly sliced

1 clove garlic, minced

1 – 2 tablespoons minced fresh ginger

2 – 3 carrots, scrubbed or peeled, and sliced into thin rounds, or cut in half lengthwise, then sliced thinly on the diagonal

1 cup shiitake mushrooms, stemmed and thinly sliced

1 tablespoon balsamic vinegar

1 teaspoon Hungarian paprika

⅓ cup goji berries

¼ cup toasted cashews

1. Bring a large pot of salted water to a boil. Cook the noodles according to the package directions. When they are tender, drain and rinse under cold water. Set aside.

2. Pile the kale leaves on top of one another, roll them up tightly and then slice into ¼ inch strips. Set aside.

3. In a wok or large skillet heat the olive oil over medium heat. Add the onions and sauté for a minute or two, then add the garlic, ginger, carrots and shiitake mushrooms. Sauté, stirring often, until the vegetables are almost tender.

4. Add the kale along with the balsamic vinegar and paprika. Continue to cook until the kale is soft and all the vegetables are tender, about five more minutes. Add the goji berries and stir. Be careful not to overcook.

5. Warm the soba noodles under hot water. Serve topped with the kale stir fry and garnish with the toasted cashews.

Serves 4 – 6

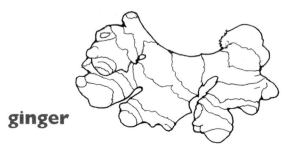

ginger

Asparagus & Mushroom Quiche

1 spelt or other whole grain pie crust

1 tablespoon olive oil

1½ cups asparagus, tough ends discarded,
    sliced into 1" lengths on the diagonal

1 cup cremini or shiitake mushrooms,
    stems cut off and thinly sliced

1 teaspoon minced garlic

1 tablespoon fresh parsley, chopped

2 teaspoons fresh dill, chopped

¾ teaspoon sea salt

3 large eggs

1 cup milk

½ cup cream or half and half

2 ounces Gruyère cheese, grated

1. Preheat the oven to 375°.
2. Sauté the asparagus in olive oil with ¼ teaspoon sea salt until just tender, 5 to 6 minutes. Don't overcook. Set aside in a bowl.
3. In the same pan, sauté the mushrooms with another ¼ teaspoon sea salt until the mushrooms are tender. Add the fresh herbs and garlic and sauté for another 30 seconds. Toss the mushrooms with the asparagus and set aside.
4. In a large bowl, whisk together the eggs, milk, half and half, ¼ teaspoon sea salt and fresh herbs.
5. Spread grated cheese on the bottom of the pie shell. Arrange the asparagus and mushroom mixture over the cheese in an even layer.
6. Pour the egg mix over the vegetables up to the rim of the pie shell.
7. Bake for 40 to 50 minutes or until the egg custard is completely set. Cool slightly before cutting.

Makes 4 – 6 servings

Do Ahead

- All of the vegetables can be prepared up to two days in advance and cooked up to a day in advance.

- The cheese can be grated up to a day in advance.

Variations

Almost anything can go into a quiche or tart. Use this basic recipe:

- 1½ to 2 cups of cooked vegetables and/or shrimp, cooked flaked salmon, diced chicken or sausage, or sliced turkey bacon;

- 3 eggs with 1¼ to 1½ cups of dairy or non-dairy milk, ¼ to ½ teaspoon sea salt, ¼ teaspoon pepper and whatever fresh herbs you'd like to use.

- ½ to ¾ cup of crumbled feta or goat cheese, or ½ to 1 cup grated cheese.

If you are including cheese, sprinkle it over the bottom of your pie shell, sprinkle the vegetables and meat over the top and then pour the egg mixture over it up to the rim. Bake until the filling is set and golden brown.

Vegetable Frittata

2 bunches chard, kale and/or collard greens, stemmed

6 cups broccoli florets and peeled stems, chopped ½ inch

1 medium onion, chopped

Olive oil for sautéing

8 eggs

1 cup milk, cream or half & half, or non-dairy milk

2 cups grated cheddar cheese, or other favorite cheese (optional)

1½ cups crumbled feta cheese (optional)

½ teaspoon sea salt

½ teaspoon pepper

3 tablespoons fresh dill, chopped, or 2 teaspoons dried dill

1. Preheat the oven to 375° and grease a 9" x 13" pan.
2. Blanch the greens in a large pot of boiling water until tender. Drain, rinse under cold water and drain well, squeezing out as much liquid as you can. Chop finely and set aside.
3. In the same pot of water, blanch the broccoli just until crisply tender. Drain, rinse under cold water, and then drain it well and add it to the greens.
4. Sauté the chopped onion in olive oil until the onion is tender and beginning to turn golden. Add the onion mixture to the vegetables, and toss to combine everything well.
5. In a separate bowl, whisk together the eggs and milk. Add the sea salt, pepper, dill and cheddar cheese (if using) and stir to combine.
6. Add the egg mixture to your vegetables and stir until everything is evenly mixed.
7. Pour the mixture into your prepared dish, then sprinkle the feta on top. Bake the frittata in a preheated oven for 40 to 45 minutes or until the frittata is set in the middle. Serve warm or at room temperature.

Serves 6 – 9

Do Ahead

- The vegetables can be prepared up to two days ahead of time, and cooked up to one day ahead of time.
- The cheese can be grated up to a day ahead of time.

Variations

You can use this basic recipe with many different combinations of ingredients. Asparagus, zucchini, sautéed mushrooms, spinach and artichoke hearts are all great additions. You can use whatever type of cheese you like or leave the cheese out all together. If you want some extra protein, try thinly sliced and sautéed turkey bacon, diced cooked shrimp or cooked, flaked salmon. Experiment using what's available in your refrigerator.

Filo with Chard, Caramelized Onions & Tofu

Do Ahead

- You can prepare all of your vegetables up to two days in advance.

- You can sauté your vegetables a day ahead of time.

- The tofu filling can be made up to two days in advance.

- The filo can be assembled a day ahead of time. Cover tightly with plastic wrap and refrigerate.

Variations

Feel free to use other vegetables in your filling but include at least one large bunch of greens. Try spinach, kale or collards as your greens, making sure to cook the kale or collards until they are tender, squeeze out all the excess water and chop finely. Add artichoke hearts, asparagus cut in 1" pieces or broccoli florets.

½ box frozen filo pastry, thawed

2 tablespoons olive oil

1 medium red or yellow onion, cut in half and then sliced very thinly

4 ounces shitake, cremini or other mushrooms, stemmed and sliced thinly (optional)

4 – 6 cloves garlic, minced

½ teaspoon sea salt

1 teaspoon fresh rosemary, minced, or ½ teaspoon dried

1 teaspoon fresh thyme, minced, or ½ teaspoon dried

1 bunch chard or other dark leafy greens, washed, stems removed and leaves finely chopped

1 pound firm tofu

1 tablespoon miso, any variety

1 teaspoon lemon zest

2 teaspoons fresh lemon juice

½ teaspoon sea salt

1 teaspoon crushed fennel seeds

¼ teaspoon nutmeg

⅛ teaspoon cinnamon

2 tablespoons olive oil

2 – 3 tablespoons water

1 teaspoon fresh oregano, chopped

1 tablespoon fresh parsley, chopped

1 tablespoon fresh basil, chopped

5 – 7 ounces goat cheese (optional)

organic olive oil spray

¼ cup pine nuts, toasted about 8 minutes in the oven, then chopped, or toasted in a small skillet on the stove top over a low flame (caution: don't leave them unattended!)

Filo with Chard

1. Heat the olive oil in a large skillet and add the onions. Cook over medium heat, stirring every so often, until the onions become translucent. Add the shiitake mushrooms and continue to cook, stirring often, until the shiitakes are almost tender. To accelerate cooking the shiitakes, add 1 or 2 tablespoons of water and cover the pan for a minute or two.

2. Add the garlic, sea salt, rosemary and thyme and cook for about 30 seconds. Add the chard and stir to mix everything together. Cover the skillet and cook for about 5 minutes, stirring every so often, until the chard is tender. If there is liquid in the pan, turn the heat up to high and cook until the liquid has evaporated and the pan is dry, or pour the vegetables into a sieve and press to remove the liquid. Set aside the vegetables.

3. Place the tofu through the fresh herbs in food processor and process until creamy, adding a bit of water if needed.

4. Combine the tofu and vegetable mixtures.

5. Grease a 9" x 13" pan and preheat your oven to 400°.

6. Open the filo and lay it flat. Carefully lift one sheet and lay it so half is in your pan and half is laying over the long side. Spray with olive oil spray, then fold the second half over. Spray that layer. Repeat this procedure with four sheets of the filo so that you have 8 layers in the pan. On two of the layers sprinkle 1 tablespoon of the toasted pine nuts.

7. Spread the filling in the pan. Crumble the goat cheese on top if you are using it.

8. Repeat the process of layering the filo, spraying each layer. Again, use four sheets folded in half so that you have 8 layers. Sprinkle 1 tablespoon of the pine nuts on two of your layers. Spray the top layer of filo with the olive spray.

9. With a sharp knife cut the uncooked filo all the way through into whatever serving sizes you want. If the filo is a main course, you might cut it down the middle and then into eight pieces. If it's a side dish, you might cut it 3 x 4 so you have 12 pieces.

10. Bake the filo in your preheated oven for 40 to 50 minutes until the top is golden brown and the filling is set.

11. Let the filo sit for about 15 minutes before serving. Using a sharp knife, cut through the places you marked earlier, and serve.

Serves 6 to 8 as a main course, or more as a side dish

"I had my first food delivery last night. I had forgotten about it so I had almond butter out for a feast of crackers and almond butter, but my stomach wasn't feeling all that great so I was waiting a bit when I got the call that the Ceres Delivery Angels were on their way. What a nice surprise.

I was immediately drawn to the sauerkraut. For some reason my stomach knew that would help. And it was right, I felt much better and then I heated up the fish entree. Wow, I felt so good by the time I was done (and I was able to eat it all). It's funny, but this organization brings me to tears more than anything. I'm so looking forward to the day when I can be a part of the giving too. But for now, I will graciously receive. Thank you!"

– Jacqui

Walnut Loaf with Burgundy Sauce

8 ounces sprouted whole grain or whole wheat bread

8 ounces walnuts

2 cups minced onion

2 tablespoons dried parsley

⅔ cup grated carrots

1 rib celery, minced

2 eggs

¾ teaspoon dried thyme

½ teaspoon dried sage

¾ teaspoon sea salt

10 ounces diced tomatoes in juice
    or about 1 cup fresh tomatoes, seeded and diced

Burgundy Sauce

3 tablespoons butter or olive oil

¼ cup flour

¼ cup red wine

2½ tablespoons tamari

1¾ cup Immune Broth or vegetable stock

1. Preheat the oven to 375° and grease a glass loaf pan.
2. Grind the bread and walnuts together in a food processor until they are fine. Place in a large bowl.
3. Add the onions, parsley, carrot, celery, eggs, seasonings and tomatoes, and mix to combine everything evenly.
4. Pack the mixture into the loaf pan and bake for 1 to 1¼ hours, or until the loaf is browned and set.
5. Cool for about 15 minutes, then carefully turn the loaf out. Cut into six or eight slices. If desired, serve with Burgundy Sauce.
6. For sauce: Melt the butter in a small saucepan. Whisk in the flour and cook, stirring, for 2 minutes. Add the wine, tamari and stock. Bring to a low boil, whisking the entire time to keep the sauce smooth. Simmer for a few minutes until it is thick and creamy. Season to taste with sea salt and pepper.

Serves 6

Do Ahead

- You can grind the bread and walnuts several days ahead of time and refrigerate in an airtight container.

- All the vegetables can be prepared a day ahead of time.

- The sauce can be made several days ahead of time and refrigerated. Warm over low heat before serving.

Variation

To make Walnut & Herb Stuffed Portobellos:

- Stem 4 large Portobello mushrooms.

- Divide the uncooked Walnut Loaf among the mushrooms, packing it to fill the cavity.

- Bake at 375° for 25 to 35 minutes or until the mushrooms are tender and the filling is set.

- Serve with the Burgundy Sauce.

Tip

Use your food processor to mince the onions and celery (cut into chunks, then place in the processor and process with on/off pulses until they are finely chopped) and to grate the carrots.

Greek Stuffed Peppers

4 bell peppers, yellow, red, orange or green

¾ cup quinoa, rinsed well and soaked for at least an hour and preferably overnight

¾ cup Immune Broth, Chicken Bone Broth, or vegetable or chicken stock, or water

1 15-ounce can chickpeas, drained and rinsed

1 tablespoon olive oil

6 ounces baby spinach leaves or young chard leaves

1 tablespoon chopped fresh oregano, or 1 teaspoon dried

¼ cup sun-dried tomatoes in oil, chopped

1 teaspoon sherry vinegar or red wine vinegar

½ teaspoon sea salt

½ cup feta cheese, crumbled (optional)

1. Preheat the oven to 350°.
2. Halve the peppers lengthwise cutting through the stems. Seed and remove the white pulp. Steam the peppers until soft but not falling apart, about 5 to 7 minutes, or cook them in a pot of boiling water for about the same length of time.
3. Bring the water and quinoa to a boil in a small saucepan. Cover, reduce the heat to low, and cook for 8 to 10 minutes until the quinoa is soft and the water is absorbed.
4. Place the chickpeas in a food processor and process using on/off pulses until they are coarsely chopped.
5. Heat the olive oil in a skillet over medium heat and add the spinach or chard and oregano. Cook, stirring, until the greens have wilted.
6. In a bowl, mix together all of the ingredients except the peppers. Divide the filling among the peppers, packing to fit.
7. Place the peppers on a baking dish and bake for about 20 minutes until they are heated through.

Serves 4 – 8, depending on what else is included

Do Ahead

- Use leftover cooked grain (about 2 cups) or cook the quinoa up to a day in advance.

- The peppers can be prepared up to a day in advance, including blanching or steaming them.

- The filling can be made up to a day in advance.

Variations

- Use the filling to stuff other vegetables. Hollow out zucchini, bake for about 20 minutes at 350°, then stuff and continue to bake until the filling is hot and the zucchini is tender. Cut an eggplant in half and roast at 350°, cut side down on a greased baking sheet. When the eggplant is almost tender, about 20 to 25 minutes, turn it over, mash the cooked eggplant slightly to create a cavity, then stuff it with the quinoa filling. Bake for another 15 to 20 minutes to heat.

- Use navy or cannellini beans instead of chick peas.

Sunny Beet & Carrot Burgers

2 cups grated beets (about ¾ pound)

2 cups grated carrots (about ½ pound)

I cup cooked brown rice

I cup grated cheddar cheese

I cup sunflower seeds, toasted

½ cup sesame seeds, toasted

2 large free-range eggs, beaten

½ cup grated onion

¼ cup olive oil

3 tablespoons all-purpose or gluten-free flour

3 tablespoons chopped parsley

3 or 4 cloves garlic, minced

2 tablespoons tamari

1. Preheat the oven to 350° and generously grease a rimmed baking sheet.
2. Mix all the ingredients in a large bowl, stirring to combine evenly.
3. Form the mixture into patties using a packed ½ cup for each. Arrange them on the baking sheet.
4. Bake the burgers for 25 to 30 minutes or until firm and the vegetables are cooked through.
5. Serve on a sprouted whole grain bun with your choice of condiments.

Makes 10 burgers

onion

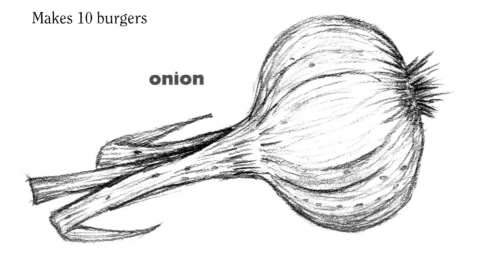

Do Ahead

- All of the vegetables can be prepared ahead of time, combined in a bowl and refrigerated.

- Cook the rice in the morning or the day before, or use leftover cooked rice.

- The sunflower and sesame seeds can be toasted several days ahead of time and refrigerated.

Variation

To make the burgers without cheese, add an additional tablespoon of flour and a bit more beaten egg.

Tip

- These burgers are a colorful and delicious surprise! Use your food processor to grate and mince the vegetables and the burgers will be quick and easy to make.

- Freeze them individually wrapped.

Thanks to Angelic Organics for the inspiration for this recipe.

Tempeh Treats

8- or 10-ounce package of tempeh

3 tablespoons extra virgin olive oil

1 tablespoon balsamic vinegar

1 tablespoon tamari

1 tablespoon fresh grated ginger or ginger juice

2 cloves garlic, minced

1. Place the tempeh in a steamer basket over boiling water and steam for 6 to 8 minutes. Alternately, place it in a small skillet with enough water to cover and bring to a simmer. Cover and cook for 6 to 8 minutes.

2. Cool slightly, then cut the tempeh into strips or cubes, and place it in an even layer in a glass baking dish. Whisk together the remaining ingredients and then pour the liquid over the tempeh. Marinate for at least an hour but preferably overnight in the refrigerator. The longer you marinate the tempeh, the more flavorful it will be.

3. When you are ready to cook it, heat 1 to 2 tablespoons olive oil in a skillet over medium heat. Remove the tempeh from the marinade and add it to the skillet. Cook the tempeh until it is golden brown and crispy on both sides. When the tempeh is done, add 1 to 2 tablespoons of the marinade and swirl the tempeh in the pan to coat it.

4. You can serve the tempeh with vegetables and a grain as a main dish, or cover it with sautéed onions and mushrooms, or add it to other grain or pasta dishes to increase the amount of protein.

Serves 2 – 4

Variations

- Try adding pineapple juice to the marinade or use sesame oil instead of olive oil for a new flavor.

- Substitute lemon juice or orange juice for the balsamic vinegar if you like.

Tips

- Serve the tempeh over brown rice or soba noodles or add to a vegetable dish.

- Tempeh Treats will keep in the refrigerator for 4 to 5 days. Reheat in a small skillet with about 1 tablespoon of water.

Chapter 8 • Seafood & Poultry

RECIPES

Turkey Loaf

Rosemary Roasted Salmon

4 – 6 salmon fillets

8 – 12 sprigs rosemary
1 red onion, very thinly sliced
2 lemons, very thinly sliced
2 – 3 tablespoons olive oil
Sea salt and pepper

1. Preheat the oven to 400°.
2. Arrange the rosemary in a single layer on a baking sheet. Cover with the red onion slices. Place the salmon on top of the onion and sprinkle with sea salt and pepper. Arrange the lemon slices on top of the salmon, then drizzle the olive oil over the top.
3. Roast in the preheated oven for about 12 to 18 minutes or until the salmon is just cooked through.

Serves 4 – 6

"By eating local, by creating relationships of integrity around food and farming, we can discover again, within ourselves, a deeper sense of responsibility toward the world – toward the earth and the livings things of the earth, including other people."

– John Ikerd

lemons

Do Ahead

The vinaigrette for the fish can be made up to two days ahead of time. Let sit at room temperature for 30 minutes before serving.

Tip

Chop the garlic and sun-dried tomatoes in a mini-processor, then add the remaining sauce ingredients and process just until creamy.

Halibut with Caper Basil Vinaigrette

4 – 6 halibut fillets, or any other firm white fish

¼ cup fresh chopped basil

¼ cup extra virgin olive oil

2 tablespoons fresh lemon juice

1 tablespoon capers

1 tablespoon chopped sun-dried tomatoes in oil

1½ teaspoons minced fresh garlic

1. Whisk the olive oil, lemon juice, basil, capers, sun-dried tomatoes and garlic together in a bowl until the sauce is creamy. Add sea salt and pepper to taste.
2. Preheat the oven to 400°. Place the fish on a greased baking pan, brush with a bit of olive oil and sprinkle with sea salt and pepper.
3. Bake the fish until it is just cooked through, about 10 to 12 minutes depending on the thickness of your fish.
4. Serve the fish garnished with a spoonful of the vinaigrette.

Serves 4 – 6

Baked Fish with Parmesan Walnut Crust

6 fish fillets such as sea bass, halibut, tilapia or cod

1 cup fresh bread crumbs

¾ cup walnuts

¼ cup finely grated Parmesan cheese

2 tablespoons loosely packed chopped fresh parsley

2 tablespoons butter or olive oil

2 tablespoons prepared horseradish

1½ tablespoons Dijon mustard

1. In a food processor, process the breadcrumbs and the walnuts using on/off pulses until the nuts are finely chopped.
2. Transfer the mixture to a bowl and stir in the cheese and parsley.
3. If you are using butter, melt it in a small saucepan and whisk in the horseradish and mustard. If you are using olive oil, simply whisk the three ingredients together.
4. Add the butter or oil mixture to the breadcrumbs and toss to coat everything evenly.
5. Place your fish fillets on a greased baking sheet. Press the topping so that it adheres evenly to the surface of each fillet.
6. Bake the fish in a preheated 400° oven just until it is cooked through and the topping is browned, 12 to 15 minutes depending on the thickness of your fish. If the fish is done and the topping isn't quite golden, place it under a broiler for 2 to 3 minutes – but keep your eye on it. Things can happen quickly when you are broiling!

Serves 6

Do Ahead

You can make the topping mixture up to two days ahead of time.

Variation

If you are not eating dairy simply use olive oil and omit the Parmesan cheese. It will still be delicious.

Spice Rubbed Fish with Thai Vinaigrette

4 fish fillets or steaks, 4 or 5 ounces each

I teaspoon chili powder

I teaspoon curry powder

I teaspoon ground coriander

I teaspoon ground cumin

I teaspoon mustard powder

I teaspoon sea salt

I teaspoon organic sugar (optional)

3 tablespoons rice vinegar

I ½ tablespoons tamari

I tablespoon toasted sesame oil

I tablespoon minced fresh cilantro

I ½ teaspoons minced fresh ginger

1. Whisk the ground herbs, sea salt and organic sugar in a small bowl, combining evenly. Place the herb mixture in a shallow dish and coat each piece of fish with the mixture.
2. Place the fillets coated side up on an oiled baking dish, cover with plastic wrap, and refrigerate for at least 30 minutes and up to 3 hours.
3. Preheat the oven to 400°. Bake the fish for 10 to 12 minutes or until it is just cooked through. The length of time will depend on the type and thickness of your fish.
4. While the fish is baking, whisk together the ingredients for the vinaigrette.
5. Serve the fish drizzled with the vinaigrette.

Serves 4

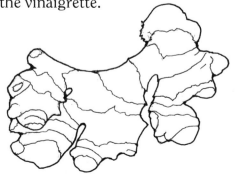

ginger

Do Ahead

- The spice mixture can be made ahead of time and stored in a sealed container for up to a month.
- The vinaigrette can be made up to three days ahead of time.

Tip

The fish is wonderful served with Coconut Rice (see below) and a sauté of fresh green vegetables such as broccoli, bok choy, zucchini and/or sugar snap peas.

Coconut Rice

Substitute coconut milk for up to half the water when cooking rice. Stir in chopped cilantro at the end and sea salt to taste.

Moroccan Herbed Fish

6 – 8 small fish steaks or fillets, about 5 or 6 ounces each

1 large bunch fresh cilantro, stemmed

1 large bunch fresh parsley, stemmed

2 tablespoons fresh minced garlic

1 teaspoon sea salt

1 tablespoon ground cumin

1 tablespoon sweet paprika

½ cup extra virgin olive oil

¼ cup fresh lemon juice

1. Roughly chop the cilantro and parsley, then place them in a food processor with the garlic and process until everything is minced. Add the sea salt, cumin, paprika, olive oil and lemon juice. Process to combine.
2. Preheat the oven to 350°. Place the fish in a greased baking dish.
3. Place the herb mixture in a small skillet and warm it over medium heat until it is very hot but not boiling. Taste and adjust the seasonings as needed. Spoon the mixture over the fish fillets. Let sit about 15 minutes.
4. Bake the fish in your preheated oven just until the fish is cooked through, 10 to 12 minutes depending on the type and thickness of your fish.

Serves 6 – 8

Do Ahead

The sauce can be made up to a day ahead of time and refrigerated. Continue with step 2 when you are ready to bake the fish.

Filet of Sole with Spinach, Shiitakes & Goat Cheese

Do Ahead

- You can wash and stem the greens, and stem and slice the mushrooms a couple days ahead of time.

- The greens can be blanched, drained and chopped, and the mushrooms sautéed, up to a day ahead of time.

- You can mix the filling together up to a day ahead of time.

1 pound English sole, each piece preferably about 2 ounces

1 bunch fresh spinach or chard, washed well and stems removed

4 ounces shiitake or cremini mushrooms, or a mixture, stemmed and sliced

1 tablespoon olive oil

1 teaspoon minced garlic

1 teaspoon balsamic vinegar

4 – 6 ounces goat cheese or Neufchâtel cheese or a blend of both

1 tablespoon minced fresh parsley (optional)

1. Steam the spinach or chard just until wilted and tender. Drain and rinse under cold water. Drain again, pressing out as much water as possible and chop fairly fine.

2. Warm the olive oil over medium heat and sauté the mushrooms just until tender. Add the garlic and balsamic vinegar and cook for another minute or two. Season to taste with sea salt and pepper.

3. Combine the cooked greens, mushrooms and cheese in a bowl, using your fingers to blend everything evenly.

4. Preheat the oven to 350°.

5. On a clean surface, lay out the fish fillets. Place 1 to 2 tablespoons of the filling in the center of each fillet and roll to enclose. Try to use all the filling but don't force it!

6. Brush the rolled fillets with a bit of olive oil and then bake for 12 to 15 minutes just until the fish is opaque and flakes easily with a fork.

7. Serve with a garnish of chopped parsley.

Serves 4 – 6

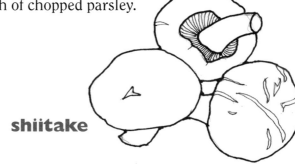

shiitake

Miso Marinated Fish with Coconut Curry Sauce

4 halibut or other firm white fish fillets

¼ cup mirin

2 tablespoons sake or white wine

2 tablespoons tamari

1 tablespoon miso (any variety)

1 tablespoon rice vinegar

½ tablespoon minced fresh ginger

1 or 2 teaspoons turbinado sugar or honey (optional)

¼ cup mirin

2 tablespoons lemongrass, minced

1½ teaspoons fresh ginger, minced

¾ – 1 cup coconut milk

1 teaspoon red or green curry paste, or to taste

¼ cup chopped fresh cilantro

1. In a blender, puree the mirin, sake, tamari, miso, rice vinegar, fresh ginger and sweetener to taste.

2. Place the fish in a glass baking dish, pour the marinade over it, and refrigerate, covered, for about two hours. Turn the fish every so often.

3. While the fish is marinating, make the coconut curry sauce. Place the mirin, lemongrass and ginger in a small saucepan and bring to a boil. Cook until the sauce is reduced by half. This will only take a few minutes.

4. Add the coconut milk and curry paste and simmer until the sauce is slightly thickened. Taste and adjust seasonings with a dash more mirin or curry paste.

5. Preheat the oven to 400°. Remove the fish from the marinade and place on a greased baking sheet. Sprinkle with sea salt and pepper. Bake just until the fish is opaque, 10 to 15 minutes depending on the thickness of your fish.

6. Serve the fish topped with coconut sauce and garnished with fresh chopped cilantro. Steamed rice and a sauté of brightly colored vegetables is a lovely accompaniment.

Serves 4

Do Ahead

Both the marinade and the sauce can be made up to two days ahead of time.

Tips

• Use your mini-processor to chop the lemongrass and ginger. Peel the ginger and slice thinly, then process. For the lemongrass, cut off the stem end, then peel the tough outer layers until you get to the tender inner core. Slice thinly, then process.

• If making two sauces feels like too much, just make one. The fish will be delicious with just the marinade, and equally delicious with just the sauce.

Seafood Vera Cruz with Lemon & Thyme

Do Ahead

- The onion, garlic and green olives can all be prepared a day or two ahead of time.

- The sauce can be made a day or two ahead of time.

Tip

This recipe makes more sauce than you probably will want for the fish. Extra sauce is excellent on whole grain pasta, some cooked chicken, sautéed vegetables or rice.

4 – 6 fish fillets, red snapper, cod, salmon or any firm white fish

2 tablespoons extra virgin olive oil

1 medium onion, peeled and thinly sliced

1 tablespoon minced garlic

3½ cups fresh tomatoes, seeded and diced
   or 1 28-ounce can of diced tomatoes, partially drained

1 tablespoon chopped fresh thyme or 1 teaspoon dried thyme

2 teaspoons lemon zest

½ cup pitted green olives, roughly sliced

2 tablespoons capers, drained

Sea salt to taste

1 – 2 pickled jalapeno peppers, stemmed, seeded and sliced
   (optional)

1. Heat the olive oil in a large skillet over medium heat. Add the onion and cook, stirring every so often, until it just begins to brown, about 5 minutes. Add the garlic and cook for another minute.

2. Raise the heat to medium high and add the tomatoes, thyme, lemon zest, olives and capers. Simmer briskly, stirring often, for about 5 minutes to evaporate some of the liquid.

3. Reduce the heat to medium low and cook for about 5 more minutes to blend the flavors. Taste and adjust the seasoning with sea salt, more lemon zest or more thyme.

4. Preheat the oven to 400°. Place the fillets on a greased baking dish. Brush or drizzle them with a bit of olive oil and sprinkle with sea salt and pepper.

5. Bake the fish for 10 to 12 minutes or until just cooked through. The length of time will depend on the type and thickness of your fish.

6. Spoon the sauce over the fish and serve.

Serves 6

Chicken with Sun-dried Tomato & Olive Pesto

6 boneless skinless chicken breasts

½ cup sun-dried tomatoes in oil, drained
½ cup pitted black olives, drained
½ small red onion, cut in chunks
¼ cup capers, drained
¼ cup olive oil
2 cloves garlic, minced

½ cup crumbled feta cheese (optional)
6 sprigs fresh parsley for garnish

1. Place the sun-dried tomatoes, olives, onion, capers, olive oil and garlic in a food processor and process until smooth.
2. Toss the chicken breasts with 2 or 3 tablespoons of the pesto, then arrange them on a greased baking sheet.
3. Spread the remaining pesto on top of the breasts so that they are covered with a thin layer.
4. Bake the chicken in a preheated 375° oven for 30 to 45 minutes until it is cooked through.
5. Top each piece of chicken with some of the crumbled feta, then garnish with a sprig of fresh parsley.

Serves 6

Do Ahead

The pesto can be made up to five days ahead of time. It will keep for at least a week in a sealed container in the refrigerator.

Tip

This pesto has many other uses. Try tossing it with rice or kamut pasta and roasted vegetables, or spread it on toasted baguette slices and top with some fresh mozzarella cheese.

Variation

You can make this entrée vegetarian by slicing tofu, marinating it briefly in a bit of tamari, and then baking it with the pesto spread on each slice.

Do Ahead

- The marinade can be made two to three days ahead of time. Remove it from the refrigerator a few hours before you want to use it so that the olive oil can liquefy.

- Marinate the chicken for up to 12 hours.

- All of the vegetables can be prepared up to a day ahead of time, including roasting them.

Variations

- This basic recipe can be used with any mix of the vegetables.

- You can make this entrée vegetarian by slicing 20 ounces of tofu 1" thick and marinating it overnight in half of the dressing. Bake until golden, 20 to 25 minutes.

Greek Chicken with Roasted Vegetables

1½ pounds boneless skinless chicken breasts

6 tablespoons extra virgin olive oil

3 tablespoons fresh lemon juice

1 to 2 tablespoons minced garlic

1½ teaspoons dried mint

1½ teaspoons dried oregano

1 teaspoon sea salt

1 teaspoon black pepper

1 or 2 yellow, red or orange bell peppers, cored and cubed 1"

1 red onion, peeled and cubed 1"

½ pound cremini mushrooms, stemmed, cut in half or quartered if large

2 medium zucchini, cut in 1" chunks

Fresh mint to garnish

1. Whisk together the olive oil, lemon juice, garlic, mint, oregano, sea salt and pepper. Toss half of the sauce with the chicken and marinate for about at least one hour and up to overnight.

2. Preheat the oven to 400°. Place the chicken on an oiled baking pan and bake until it is just cooked through, 25 to 35 minutes depending on the size of your breasts. Let cool slightly.

3. While the chicken is cooking, toss the remaining dressing with the vegetables. Spread them in a single layer on another baking sheet and roast in the oven for about 20 to 25 minutes or until the vegetables are tender and beginning to brown.

4. When the chicken has cooled slightly, slice it against the grain and toss it with the roast vegetables. Serve garnished with chopped fresh mint.

Serves 4 – 6

Herb Crusted Lemon Chicken

2 boneless skinless chicken breasts, tenders removed
and each cut in half crosswise

¼ cup fresh lemon juice

1 tablespoon butter

1 tablespoon olive oil

½ – ¾ cup dried bread crumbs or very finely ground fresh ones

3 tablespoons minced fresh basil

3 tablespoons minced fresh parsley

1½ tablespoons minced fresh rosemary

½ teaspoon sea salt

¼ teaspoon black pepper

1. Place each piece of chicken between two sheets of parchment or waxed paper and pound with a mallet until they are an even ½" thick. Toss the chicken pieces with the lemon juice until they are evenly coated. Refrigerate, covered, one hour or as long as overnight.

2. When you are ready to bake the chicken, preheat the oven to 450°.

3. Melt the butter and olive oil together in a small dish, or use only olive oil.

4. Toss the bread crumbs, herbs and sea salt and pepper together in a large shallow bowl.

5. Remove each piece of chicken from the lemon juice, brush it on both sides with the butter and olive oil mixture or with just olive oil, and then place it in the bowl of breadcrumbs and herbs. Coat both sides of the chicken with the herb mixture, pressing to help the herbs adhere.

6. Place the coated chicken on a baking sheet and bake until it is cooked through and golden brown, 12 to 15 minutes depending on the thickness of your chicken.

Serves 4 – 6

Do Ahead

- The chicken can be pounded a day ahead of time, and marinated either the day before or in the morning.

- The herbed bread crumb mixture can be made in the morning.

Tips

- Make a double recipe and freeze individual pieces of the cooked chicken for later use.

- If you are feeling weak, ask your butcher to pound the chicken breasts for you.

Do Ahead

- Make the chicken marinade up to two or three days ahead of time.

- Marinate the chicken up to a day ahead of time.

- Prep the raw vegetables up to a day ahead of time.

- You can cook the rice up to a day ahead of time or use rice that is already cooked. Warm it in a covered saucepan with a bit of water, then proceed as above.

Miso Glazed Chicken with Vegetable Rice

4 skinless boneless chicken breasts

½ cup white miso

3 tablespoons brown rice syrup, honey, or turbinado sugar

¼ cup Immune Broth, Chicken Bone Broth, or vegetable or chicken stock, or water

3 tablespoons regular sesame oil (not toasted)

1 tablespoon minced ginger

1 cup brown rice, soaked for at least an hour and up to overnight, then drained

1 – 2 cups shredded Napa cabbage

1 carrot, peeled and shredded

½ cup diced red, orange or yellow bell pepper

¼ cup rice vinegar

1 teaspoon sea salt

1. In a bowl large enough to hold the chicken, whisk together the miso, brown rice syrup, broth, sesame oil and ginger. Add the chicken and toss to coat evenly. Cover the chicken and refrigerate for at least an hour and as long as overnight.

2. While the chicken is marinating, bring 1¾ cup broth or water to a boil with the drained, soaked rice in a medium-sized saucepan. Reduce the heat to low, cover, and cook until the rice is tender and all the water is absorbed, about 30 minutes.

3. Preheat the oven to 375°. Place the chicken on a cookie sheet lined with foil. Fold up the edges of the foil and pour the marinade over the chicken. Bake for 25 to 35 minutes or until the chicken is cooked through.

4. Toss the vegetables with the rice vinegar and sea salt and set aside.

5. When the rice is cooked, combine the vegetables with the warm rice and toss to combine.

6. Let the chicken sit for about 5 minutes and then slice each breast thinly against the grain.

7. Arrange the rice and vegetable mixture on four plates and top with the sliced chicken breast and remaining marinade. Serve with tamari on the side.

Serves 4

Oven "Fried" Buttermilk Chicken

6 pieces of chicken, bone-in or boneless, breasts, thighs, legs, whatever you prefer

½ cup buttermilk

2 tablespoons olive oil

1 tablespoon Dijon mustard

1 teaspoon Tabasco or other hot sauce (optional)

1 clove garlic, minced

1 teaspoon sea salt

¼ teaspoon black pepper

½ onion, sliced thinly

1 cup dry breadcrumbs

⅓ cup finely grated Parmesan cheese (optional but delicious)

¼ cup unbleached flour, rice or whole wheat are fine

2 teaspoons dried thyme

½ teaspoon paprika

3 tablespoons melted butter or olive oil

1. Mix together the buttermilk, olive oil, Dijon, hot sauce, garlic, sea salt, pepper and onion slices. Add the chicken pieces and turn to coat evenly. Cover and chill for at least 3 hours or, preferably, overnight.
2. Preheat the oven to 425°.
3. Combine the breadcrumbs, Parmesan cheese, flour, thyme and paprika in a shallow wide bowl.
4. Remove the chicken from the marinade, allowing any excess to run off. Coat the chicken in the breadcrumb mixture and place it on a greased baking sheet.
5. Drizzle each piece with some of the melted butter and/or olive oil.
6. Bake the chicken until it is crisp and golden and reaches an internal temperature of 160°, about 30 to 40 minutes.

Serves 6

Do Ahead

- Start preparing this the day before and let the chicken marinate overnight for the best results.

- The bread crumb coating can also be assembled the day before and stored in the refrigerator in a covered container.

Variation

This is also a great way to prepare white fish fillets such as catfish, snapper or cod. The fish will take just 10 to 12 minutes to cook. Marinate the fish for at least 30 minutes and up to two hours but not overnight.

Tip

The baked chicken makes wonderful leftovers that can be enjoyed cold or warm.

Do Ahead

- Bake the chicken up to a day ahead of time.
- Make the sauce up to two days ahead of time.

Variation

You can also add steamed or sautéed vegetables to the sauce along with the chicken. Try sautéed mushrooms and onions, peas, steamed sugar snap or snow peas, or steamed carrots.

Chicken with Ginger Lime Sauce

1 pound boneless skinless chicken breasts

1 tablespoon fresh lime juice

¾ teaspoon toasted sesame oil

¾ teaspoon tamari

1 – 2 teaspoons fresh minced ginger

1 teaspoon rice vinegar

1 teaspoon red wine vinegar

½ teaspoon honey (optional)

1 tablespoon peanut butter
 (use tahini if you are allergic to peanuts)

2 tablespoons peanut, sunflower or regular sesame oil
 (not toasted)

1 tablespoon fresh minced cilantro

1. Lightly season the chicken with sea salt and pepper and bake in a 350° oven for 25 to 35 minutes or until cooked through. Cool and then thinly slice.
2. While the chicken is baking, place the lime juice, sesame oil, tamari, ginger, rice vinegar, red wine vinegar, honey, peanut butter and cilantro in the bowl of a food processor and process until combined. With the processor running, slowing pour in the peanut or other oil until the sauce is creamy.
3. Toss the chicken with the sauce and warm gently in a 350° oven or in a small covered skillet over low heat. Serve with steamed brown rice.

Serves 4

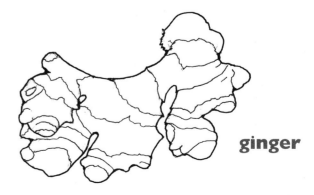

ginger

Chicken in Orange, Ginger & Lemongrass Sauce

1 pound boneless skinless chicken breast

1 tablespoon tamari

1 tablespoon sesame oil

¾ cup fresh orange juice

1 teaspoon cornstarch

1 teaspoon olive oil

¼ cup onion, finely chopped

2 tablespoons fresh ginger, minced

2 tablespoons lemongrass, minced*

1 tablespoon garlic, minced

⅛ teaspoon red chili flakes (optional)

¼ cup Immune Broth, Chicken Bone Broth, or vegetable or chicken stock, or water

1 tablespoon tamari

2 tablespoons toasted sesame seeds

1. Toss the chicken with an equal mixture of tamari and sesame oil. Place on baking sheets and bake at 375° until cooked through (25 to 30 minutes). Cool and slice the chicken thinly.

2. In a small bowl, whisk 2 tablespoons of the orange juice with the cornstarch and set aside.

3. Heat the olive oil in a saucepan. Add the onion, ginger, lemongrass, garlic and the optional red chilies and sauté until the onion is golden, stirring often, 5 to 10 minutes.

4. Add the rest of the orange juice, broth or water, and tamari. Bring the sauce to a boil and cook until it is reduced slightly, about 5 to 8 minutes. Whisk in the cornstarch mixture and cook for another minute until the sauce thickens. Season with sea salt and pepper.

5. Toss the sliced chicken with the sauce and serve with brown rice and a mixture of colorful vegetables. Sprinkle everything with sesame seeds.

Serves 4

Do Ahead

• The sauce can be made up to two days ahead of time.

• The chicken can be baked and sliced up to a day ahead of time.

Tips

• This sauce is also delicious on a firm fish such as salmon, sea bass or halibut.

• Use a mini-processor to chop the onion, ginger, lemongrass and garlic. For the lemongrass, cut off the stem end, then peel the tough outer layers until you get to the tender inner core. Slice thinly, then process.

* Lemongrass is available in the produce section of most grocery stores and Asian markets. You will need about one stalk.

Do Ahead

- Prepare your vegetables up to a day ahead of time, and feel free to sauté them then as well.

- Use your food processor to make the bread crumbs and to chop the vegetables.

Variations

- This loaf can be made with ground chicken as well but it will not be quite as moist.

- If you have access to a good quality meat department that makes their own organic chicken and turkey sausage, substitute ¼ to ½ pound sausage for an equal amount of ground turkey. The flavor of the sausage you choose will influence the flavor of the final loaf. Try a sweet apple sausage or one with Italian or pesto flavors.

Turkey Loaf

1¼ pound ground turkey

½ cup fresh bread crumbs
  (use rice bread if you are gluten sensitive)
1 tablespoon olive oil
½ medium onion, finely chopped
1 small carrot, scrubbed or peeled and finely chopped
1 stalk celery, finely chopped
2 teaspoons finely chopped garlic
¼ teaspoon black pepper
½ teaspoon ground cumin
½ teaspoon sea salt
¼ teaspoon ground nutmeg
⅛ teaspoon cayenne pepper
1 egg, beaten lightly
3 tablespoons tomato sauce or purée, or 1 tablespoon tomato paste whisked together with two tablespoons water
3 tablespoons dairy or non-dairy milk

1. Preheat the oven to 375° and oil a Pyrex loaf pan.
2. Place the ground turkey and bread crumbs in a large bowl.
3. Sauté all the vegetables, except the garlic, over medium heat in 1 tablespoon olive oil until tender, about 10 minutes. Add the garlic and cook for another minute. Set aside to cool.
4. While the vegetables are cooling, sprinkle all the spices over the meat and bread crumbs.
5. Add the egg, tomato sauce and milk, then the cooled vegetables. Using your hands, mix everything together for several minutes until the ingredients are thoroughly incorporated.
6. Pack the turkey mixture into the loaf pan and pat it to level the top.
7. Bake the loaf in the preheated oven at 375° for 50 minutes to an hour, or until the internal temperature of the loaf reaches 170°.
8. Let the loaf rest for about 10 minutes before slicing.

Serves 4 – 6

Chapter 9•Delectable Desserts

RECIPES

Gingerbread Cookies

Goji Stuffed Baked Apples with Orange Zest

6 large apples, washed and cored

2 tablespoons goji berries

4 dates, chopped

1 orange, zest and juice

⅓ cup quinoa or oat flakes

½ cup almonds, toasted and chopped

3 teaspoons butter or coconut oil

1 teaspoon ground cinnamon

½ teaspoon ground cardamom

¼ teaspoon ground ginger

¼ teaspoon ground cloves

1. Preheat the oven to 350°. Arrange the apples in a 9" x 13" baking dish.
2. Zest the rind of the orange and then juice it. Soak the goji berries and dates in the orange juice and zest.
3. Combine the quinoa or oat flakes, almonds, butter or oil and spices. Add the goji berry mixture and combine thoroughly.
4. Fill the apples with the mixture.
5. Cover the apples with foil and bake for 35 to 45 minutes or until the apples are tender.

Serves 6

Do Ahead

- The orange can be zested and the dates and goji berries soaked the day before.

- The almonds can be toasted and chopped a few days ahead of time and refrigerated.

- The filling mixture can be assembled a day ahead of time.

Poached Winter Fruits

1½ cups water

¼ – ½ cup organic maple syrup or honey

Zest of 1 orange

6 whole cloves

2 cinnamon sticks, about 2" each

4 ripe but firm pears, peeled, cored and quartered

4 apples, peeled, cored and quartered

2 dried Calimyrna figs, quartered

¼ cup dried cherries

1. Combine the first five ingredients in a large pot and bring to a simmer.
2. Add the pears and apples and cook for about 10 minutes, or until the fruit is just barely tender.
3. Add the dried fruit and cook another 10 minutes or so until the fruit is tender and the syrup has reduced by half.
4. Serve the fruit warm or chilled.

Serves 4 – 6

"The new agrarian movement that is now sweeping this country embodies many of the most critical elements of a healthy society: reverence, mystery, humility, ecology in its wider sense, and community."

– Michael Abelman

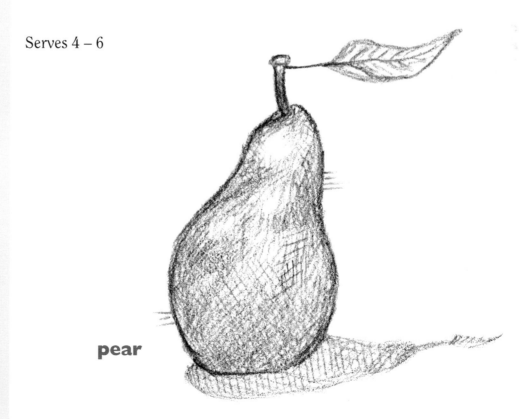

pear

Ginger Crisp
with Apples or Pears

8 large pears or apples

¼ cup maple syrup or honey

1 teaspoon almond extract

2 teaspoons freshly grated or minced ginger

Zest of 1 orange

½ cup apple juice or cider

1 tablespoon arrowroot, tapioca flour or corn starch

2 cups rolled oats

1 cup whole wheat, spelt or rice flour

1 cup almonds, toasted and chopped

Pinch of sea salt

⅓ cup almond or walnut oil

¼ – ½ cup maple syrup or honey

1 teaspoon almond extract

1. Preheat the oven to 350°. Peel, core and slice the pears or apples and place them in a large greased casserole dish or 9" x 13" pan.

2. In a bowl, combine the syrup, almond extract, ginger, orange zest and apple juice. Whisk in the arrowroot until smooth. Pour over the fruit and set aside.

3. In a separate bowl, combine the oats, flour, almonds and a pinch of sea salt. Separately, whisk together the oil, syrup and almond extract. Add the liquid to the oat mixture and toss to combine evenly.

4. Sprinkle the oat topping over the pears. Cover with foil and bake for 35 minutes. Remove the foil and bake another 15 minutes or until the topping is browned and the fruit is tender.

Serves 8

Do Ahead

- You can mix the topping ingredients together a day ahead of time.

- The almonds can be toasted and chopped several days ahead of time and refrigerated.

Tip

Ginger Crisp is wonderful for breakfast. Warm in a 350° oven for 15 minutes and then top with yogurt or kefir.

Pear & Sweet Potato Upside-down Pie

Do Ahead

- The topping can be mixed together up to two days in advance and stored, covered, in the refrigerator.

- The fruit and sweet potatoes can be prepared the night before or in the morning, tossed with the lemon juice, and refrigerated in a covered container.

Tip

This recipe has no added sugar. It's great for breakfast or as a snack anytime throughout the day.

Filling

4 pears, cored and sliced about ¼" thick

2 medium sweet potatoes, peeled and sliced into ¼" thick rounds

¼ cup goji berries

1 tablespoon fresh lemon juice

¾ cup apple or orange juice, or apple cider

2 – 3 tablespoons freshly grated ginger (optional)

¾ teaspoon ground cinnamon

1 tablespoon tapioca flour, arrowroot or cornstarch

¼ teaspoon sea salt

Almond Top Crust

2 cups almonds, finely ground in a food processor

¼ cup wheat, spelt or rice flour

2 cups rolled oats or quinoa flakes

1 tablespoon ground cinnamon

½ cup melted coconut oil or ghee

3 tablespoons apple or orange juice

1 teaspoon vanilla extract

1. Preheat the oven to 375° and grease a 9" x 13" baking dish.
2. Combine all the filling ingredients in a large bowl, tossing gently so that everything is coated evenly. Spread the filling in your prepared dish.
3. Combine all the topping ingredients in a separate bowl, then spread them evenly over the filling.
4. Bake for 45 to 60 minutes, or until the filling is soft and the topping is crisp and golden.

Serves 8

Triple Berry Pie

Crust

6 tablespoons cold butter

1½ cups whole wheat pastry flour or a mixture of flours
(oat, spelt, rice, almond meal, unbleached white)

6 tablespoons ice water

Filling

2 cups fresh or frozen raspberries
~ or ~ blueberries, strawberries or loganberries

3 cups fresh or frozen blackberries

¼ cup goji berries

1 cup raw honey or brown rice syrup

1 teaspoon ground cinnamon

¼ cup plus 2 teaspoons arrowroot or cornstarch

1. Preheat the oven to 450° and lightly grease an 11¾" x 7½" glass baking dish. Defrost the berries if they are frozen.

2. Place the flour in a food processor. Cube the butter and add it. Process with on/off pulses just until the mixture looks crumbly. Add the ice water, one tablespoon at a time, and process briefly just until the mixture forms a ball. Don't over-process.

3. Roll out half the dough on a floured surface to fit your prepared pan. Line the pan with the dough.

4. In a large bowl mix together all the berries with the honey, cinnamon and arrowroot or cornstarch. Let it sit for 15 minutes to allow the juices to come out. If it is very juicy add 1 or 2 more teaspoons of arrowroot or cornstarch.

5. Pour the filling into the crust in the prepared pan.

6. Roll out the remaining dough and lay it over the bottom crust, crimping the edges together. Cur two or three slits in the crust.

7. Bake at 450° for 10 minutes, then reduce the heat to 350° and continue baking for another 35 to 40 minutes or until the crust is golden and the filling is thick and bubbling.

Serves 6 – 8

Variation

You can also bake the filling in a purchased pre-made spelt or whole wheat pie crust. Cover the filling with a second pre-made crust or with some crumble topping from the Ginger Crisp with Apples or Pears on page xx.

Dairy Free Soft "Ice Cream"

Banana Raspberry

5 bananas, peeled and frozen

¼ cup fresh or frozen raspberries

1. Process the frozen bananas and raspberries in a Champion juicer with the blank cartridge so that the fruit exits as a purée after running through the juicer. Enjoy!
2. Alternately, break up the bananas and process in a food processor using on/off pulses until the mixture is creamy but not melted.

Banana Coconut

5 bananas, peeled and frozen

1 15-ounce can coconut milk

¼ cup coconut cream or coconut flakes

1 teaspoon vanilla extract

1 – 2 tablespoons honey or maple syrup (optional)

1. Put everything except the bananas in the blender and process until it is smooth and creamy. Freeze the mixture in ice cube trays.
2. Remove from the freezer before processing and allow the coconut cubes to soften.
3. Process the bananas and the cubes in a Champion juicer with the blank cartridge so that the mixture exits as a purée.
4. Alternately, break up the banana and process in a food processor with the slightly softened coconut cubes using on/off pulses until the mixture is creamy but not melted.

Serves 4

> *"Dear Ceres Angels,*
>
> *This has been a wonderful help and blessing having healthy food available during my weakest time. Thank you!"*
>
> — Sandy

Chocolate Banana Pudding

1 12.5-ounce package Mori Nu silken firm tofu

1 teaspoon vanilla extract

1 ripe banana, chopped

½ cup organic dark chocolate chips

1. Melt the chocolate chips in a small Pyrex cup in a pot of simmering water, stirring often until they are melted. Set aside.
2. Place the tofu and vanilla in a food processor and process until the tofu is very smooth, scraping the bowl several times.
3. Add the banana and process again until everything is very smooth.
4. Scrape all the melted chocolate into the tofu mixture and process just to combine evenly.
5. Refrigerate the pudding for at least two hours, then enjoy.

Serves 3 – 4

Variations

- Omit the banana if you prefer. The pudding is also delicious with a garnish of fresh berries.

- If you can not find good quality organic dark chocolate chips, substitute ½ cup of chopped 70% organic dark chocolate.

Thanks to *Clean Food* by Terry Walters for the inspiration for this wonderful recipe.

Chocomole

2 ripe avocados

20 dates

2 tablespoons maple syrup or honey, or to taste

¼ teaspoon vanilla extract

1 tablespoon coconut oil

1½ teaspoons raw cacao powder, or more to taste

1. Chop the dates roughly, then place them in a food processor and process until they are finely chopped.
2. Cut the avocados in half, remove the stone and scoop the flesh into the food processor. Reserve the skins.
3. Add the sweetener, vanilla, coconut oil and cacao powder to the processor and process with on/off pulses until the pudding is creamy.
4. Pack the pudding back into the avocado skins or in a bowl. Cover and refrigerate for at least a couple of hours and preferably overnight.

Serves 4

"The Healing Foods Cooking Course was a bouquet of goodness for my spirit, soul and body. The camaraderie of quality people added to my experience like the icing on the cake!"

– Mercedes

avocado

Lily's Coconut Pudding

2½ tablespoons cornstarch

1 15-ounce can coconut milk

1 egg yolk

⅓ cup maple syrup

Pinch of sea salt

1 teaspoon vanilla

1. Dissolve the cornstach in 1/3 cup of the milk, then whisk in the egg yolk. Set aside.
2. Mix the remaining coconut milk, sweetener and pinch of sea salt in a saucepan. Heat over medium heat just until it's about to boil.
3. Whisk about ¼ cup of the hot milk into the egg yolk mixture, then pour the egg mixture into the hot milk in a steady stream, whisking constantly.
4. Continue to cook over medium heat, stirring constantly, until the pudding thickens, 3 to 5 minutes.
5. Remove the pudding from the heat and stir in the vanilla. Pour the pudding into a bowl, cover the surface with wax paper or saran wrap, and refrigerate until the pudding is cold.

Serves 4

"I left the Ceres Project's Healing Foods Cooking Class and headed to my home which is still in the midst of the moving in chaos. There was one thought, one vision – the sacred space of my kitchen. Rather than doing my usual "quiet time" on zafu, I slowly and quietly arranged counter spaces, drawers, pantry shelves. . . . ahhh! When I woke in the morning and walked into this emerging sacred space to make tea, it blessed my entire day. Thank you for the inspiration!"

– Nita

Rice Pudding

1 cup organic cultured sour cream

4 eggs

¼ cup cashews, soaked for at least an hour in 1 cup water, then drained

1 cup almond milk or other non-dairy milk

1 cup cooked brown rice

⅓ cup honey or organic maple syrup

1 tablespoon ground cinnamon

¼ cup goji berries

½ cup currants or raisins

1. Preheat the oven to 350° and lightly grease a 1½ quart baking dish such as an 8" x 8," 9" x 9," or 11" x 7" pan.
2. In a large bowl, whisk together the eggs and the sour cream until the mixture is smooth.
3. In a blender, combine the drained cashews and the almond milk and blend until the cashews are very finely ground. Add the almond cashew milk to the sour cream and egg mixture.
4. Mix in the rice, sweetener, cinnamon and dried fruit. Stir to combine evenly.
5. Pour the mixture into the prepared baking dish and bake for 30 to 35 minutes or until the pudding is thick and golden.

Serves 6 – 8

Flourless Chocolate Cake

1 15-ounce can chickpeas, drained and rinsed

½ teaspoon baking soda

1½ cups dark chocolate chips or bits of broken up dark chocolate

¾ cup sweetener: honey, brown rice syrup, turbinado sugar or sucanat

3 large eggs, beaten

1. Preheat the oven to 350°.
2. In a food processor or blender fitted with the "S" blade, mash the chickpeas.
3. Add the sweetener, baking soda and chocolate and quickly blend them into the chickpea mash.
4. Add the beaten eggs and pulse until they are integrated into the batter. It will look like cake batter.
5. Pour the batter into an ungreased 8" x 8" square pan. If you like, grate some chocolate on the top.
6. Bake the cake for 25 to 30 minutes. The cake will be springy but firm in the center, just like a cake made with flour!

Serves 9

"[Eating locally for the past year] permanently altered the way I eat. In more ways than one, it left a good taste in my mouth. That good taste was satisfaction. The time I spent getting the food and preparing it was not, in the end, a cost at all. In the end it was a benefit, the benefit. In my role as eater, I was part of something larger than myself that made sense to me – a community. I felt grounded, connected."

– **Bill McKibben**,
Deep Economy

Thanks to an anonymous nutritionist at the 2009 Cancer Guides conference for this wonderful recipe!

Banana Chocolate Chip Cookies

2 bananas, mashed

¼ cup almond or walnut oil

¼ cup maple syrup

½ teaspoon vanilla

1 cup rolled oats

⅔ cup whole wheat, spelt or brown rice flour

¼ teaspoon baking soda

½ cup shredded unsweetened coconut

Pinch sea salt

¼ cup organic dark chocolate chips or
  ¼ cup chopped 70% dark chocolate

1. Preheat the oven to 350°.
2. In a medium mixing bowl, combine the banana, oil, syrup and vanilla.
3. In another bowl, combine the oats, flour, baking soda, coconut and sea salt.
4. Add the liquid ingredients to the dry and blend just to combine (don't over mix). Stir in the chocolate chips.
5. Drop the batter onto a greased baking sheet, using about one heaping teaspoon of batter per cookie. There is no need to roll, flatten or shape them. Bake the cookies for 14 to 16 minutes, or until golden brown and set. Transfer to a wire rack to cool.

Makes about 18 cookies

Adapted from *Clean Food* by Terry Walters.

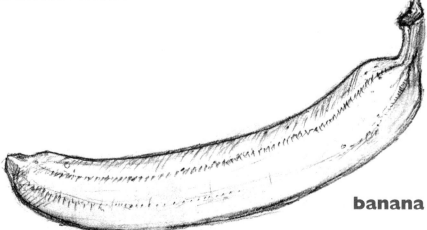

banana

Almond Oatmeal Thumbprints

½ pound raw almonds

I cup regular rolled oats

I cup whole wheat pastry flour or refined spelt flour

2 teaspoons cinnamon

I teaspoon baking soda

¼ cup almond oil

6 tablespoons maple syrup, honey or brown rice syrup

¼ cup almond milk

⅓ cup apricot jam or any other flavor you like

1. Preheat the oven to 350°.
2. Finely grind the almonds and oats in a food processor.
3. In a large bowl, combine the almond oat mixture with the flour, cinnamon and baking soda. Stir to mix evenly.
4. In a small bowl, whisk together the almond oil, maple syrup and milk. Add to the dry ingredients and stir to combine thoroughly. Let the dough rest for 10 to 15 minutes.
5. Roll the dough into small balls, using about 1 tablespoon of dough for each. Place them on a baking sheet lined with parchment paper. With your thumb, press the center of each ball to make a well. Fill each with ½ teaspoon of jam.
6. Bake the cookies for 15 to 20 minutes or until they are set and lightly browned. Transfer to a wire rack to cool.

Makes about 36 cookies

Tip

Choose a jam or fruit spread that is made without added sugars.

Tip

To decorate the cookies, brush them with mixed egg whites before baking and then shake on sprinkles, or use raisins, currants, chocolate chips, cranberries and whole or chopped nuts.

"Scientific reductionism is an undeniably powerful tool, but it can mislead us too, especially when applied to something as complex as, on the one side, a food, and on the other, a human eater. It encourages us to take a mechanistic view of that transaction: put in this nutrient; get out that physiological result. Yet people differ in important ways.

The culture of the kitchen, as embodied in those enduring traditions we call cuisines, contains more wisdom about diet and health than you are apt to find in any nutrition journal or journalism."

– Michael Pollan

Gingerbread Cookies

½ cup unsalted butter
½ cup honey
½ cup blackstrap molasses

½ teaspoon ground cinnamon
¼ teaspoon ground nutmeg
¼ teaspoon ground cloves
¼ teaspoon freshly grated ginger or
   ⅜ teaspoon ground ginger
½ teaspoon baking soda dissolved in ¼ cup hot water

2¾ cups whole wheat pastry flour
Extra flour for rolling the cookies

1. Cream together the butter, honey and black strap molasses. Add the spices to the creamed mixture and mix well. Mix in the dissolved baking soda to the creamed mixture. Stir in the flour and blend until smooth.
2. Chill the dough for at least an hour.
3. Preheat the oven to 325°. Lightly grease a cookie sheet.
4. Working with ¼ of the dough at a time, roll out the dough on a lightly floured surface until it is ¼" thick. Cut out shapes using cookie cutters and place them on a greased cookie sheet. Bake for 15 to 20 minutes. Cool before removing from the cookie sheets.
5. Repeat using all the dough and dough scraps.

Makes 2 – 4 dozen cookies depending on what size cookie cutter you use.

Cashew Cardamom Balls

1 cup lightly toasted cashew pieces

¼ teaspoon ground cardamom, or to taste

1 cup finely chopped dates

Zest of one orange

1 cup unsweetened coconut

1. Toast the coconut in a small heavy skillet over low heat, stirring often until it is golden and fragrant. Let cool.
2. Place the cashews and half the coconut in a food processor and process until the cashews are very finely ground and the coconut is almost powdered.
3. Stir in the cardamom, dates and orange peel. Knead the mixture with your fingers until uniform. Form into 1" balls and then roll in the remaining coconut.

Makes 18 balls

Tip

If the mixture seems too dry, add 1 to 2 teaspoons of almond oil. If it doesn't hold together, add a dash of maple syrup or a bit more chopped dates.

Variations

- You can use other dried fruits, including figs, dried apples or dried cherries instead of the fruits listed.

- To make them more child friendly, add ¼ to ½ cup unsweetened cocoa powder and 1 teaspoon of vanilla or almond extract.

Energy Balls

These quick whole-food energy balls travel well and provide a concentrated source of nutrition.

Basic Ingredients

2 cups almond, peanut, cashew or sesame butter

3 tablespoons flax, chia or hemp seeds, soaked for 30 minutes and then drained

1 cup pitted dates

½ cup dried apricots

½ cup raisins

¼ cup honey (optional)

1 – 2 tablespoons blackstrap molasses (optional)

¼ cup goji berries, soaked for 30 minutes, then drained

2 tablespoons dried green food supplement such as Vitamineral Green (see Resource Guide)

¼ – ½ cup juice, tea, or water to make it smoother

Pinch of cardamom or cinnamon

1 tablespoon nutritional yeast or protein powder (optional)

2 tablespoons bee pollen (optional)

Rolling Ingredients

2 cups shredded unsweetened coconut

½ cup sesame seeds or finely ground nuts

1. Place the basic ingredients into a food processor and process until it is smooth and evenly combined, adding the juice, water or tea as needed to get a firm but roll-able consistency.
2. Roll into balls, using about 1 tablespoon of the mixture at a time. You may want to wet your hands slightly to prevent sticking.
3. Roll the balls in shredded coconut, sesame seeds or ground nuts.
4. Refrigerate in an airtight container with wax or parchment paper between the layers.

Makes about 24 balls

Chapter 10•Specialty Foods

RECIPES

Immune Broth

Immune Broth

6 unpeeled carrots with green tops if possible, cut in thirds

3 medium unpeeled onions, cut in chunks

1 bunch celery, root end trimmed and cut in thirds

6 unpeeled cloves garlic

1 large bunch parsley

2 red potatoes, quartered

2 large yams or sweet potatoes, cut in chunks

2 teaspoons sea salt

3" piece of kombu seaweed

3 bay leaves

6 black peppercorns

2 allspice or juniper berries

1 handful of organic goji berries

Optional Herbs

½ ounce (15 grams) dried sliced reishi mushrooms

1 ounce (30 grams) dried codonopsis root

1 ounce (30 grams) astragalus root slices

1 small piece Panax ginseng

1. Place all the ingredients in a large soup pot. Cover with 8 or 9 quarts of water and bring to a boil.
2. Reduce the heat to low, partially cover, and simmer for at least two hours and up to four, adding more water if needed.
3. Let the broth cool, then strain the stock with a fine mesh strainer.
4. Package the broth in containers and store in the refrigerator or freezer.

Makes about 6 quarts

Tips

- See the Resource Guide for mail order sources of high quality organic herbs.

- Immune Broth and Chicken Bone Broth will keep for one week in your refrigerator or up to two months if frozen in an air-tight container.

This recipe is adapted from Rebecca Katz's recipe for Magic Mineral Broth in her cookbook, *One Bite at a Time: Nourishing Recipes for Cancer Survivors and their Caregivers.*

Chicken Bone Broth

Variations

Optional herbs:

- ¼-ounce (7–8 grams) dried sliced reishi mushrooms
- ½-ounce dried codonopsis root
- ½-ounce astragalus root
- 1 small piece Panax ginseng

Tip

Use Immune Broth or Chicken Bone Broth instead of water when cooking grains or making soup.

1 whole grass-fed organic chicken, cut in quarters, or 2 – 3 pounds of bony chicken parts such as wings, necks and backs

5 quarts cold water

2 tablespoons apple cider vinegar or lemon juice

3" piece kombu sea vegetable

1 large onion, chopped

2 carrots, chopped

3 stalks celery, chopped

1 bay leaf

6 black peppercorns

2 allspice or juniper berries

1. Place the chicken and water in a large stock pot. Bring it to a boil and then simmer until the meat is tender and will easily fall off the bones, about one and a half to two hours.
2. Strain the broth into another pot and place the chicken parts in a bowl.
3. Let the chicken cool and remove the meat from the bones. Refrigerate the meat.
4. Put the bones back into the pot with the broth. Add the apple cider vinegar or the lemon juice, the Kombu, vegetables, and whatever herbs you want to use.
5. Bring the pot to a boil and then reduce the heat to very low. Cover and simmer for 12 to 24 hours or more, until the marrow is out of the bones. The longer you cook the broth, the more nutrient rich it will be. Check the water level every couple of hours and add water as needed.
6. Strain the broth, removing the bones and vegetable matter.
7. Cool the broth completely and place it in the refrigerator. The fat will come to the top and you can remove it with a spoon.
8. Place the Bone Broth in storage containers and keep refrigerated or freeze.

Makes 2 – 3 quarts of rich bone broth

Fennel Carrot Congee

Congee is a nourishing thin porridge. It is especially beneficial when you are debilitated by illness and don't have an appetite. This particular congee supports the digestive system and can be simplified by cooking just the rice and broth.

1 cup brown or white basmati rice

5 cups Immune or Chicken Bone Broth, or
    vegetable or chicken stock

¼ cup chopped fennel

1 carrot, chopped or sliced

1. Place the water, vegetables, and rice in a slow cooker or rice cooker.
2. Cook for 4 to 6 hours on the lowest possible temperature, adding water as needed to maintain a soup-like consistency.

Makes 5 cups

Variations

- Garnish with chopped cilantro and/or sliced green onions.

- Add fish, chicken or tempeh for added protein.

- Add ½ cup sliced shiitake mushrooms, onions or leeks.

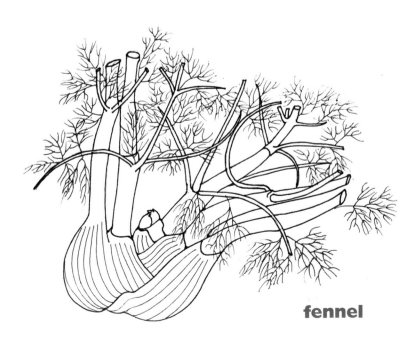

fennel

Tips

- It is recommended that you eat one Vitality Truffle daily. This amount provides what is traditionally considered a therapeutic dose of the herbs.

- See the Resource Guide for sources of high quality herbs.

About Adaptogens

The herbs included in our Vitality Truffles are considered tonics and have been used for centuries in both Ayurveda and Traditional Chinese Medicine to enhance vitality and well-being. Modern herbalists call them adaptogens. Adaptogens are a class of herbs which provide system-wide resistance to a broad range of factors, enhance our capacity to manage emotional, physical and environmental stress, and have a normalizing or balancing effect on the body.

Vitality Truffles

1½ cups almonds, soaked for 12 hours, drained and then baked in a 200° oven for 2 – 4 hours

¾ cup coconut oil, melted

⅓ – ½ cup honey

1 cup shredded coconut

6 tablespoons eleuthero powder

⅓ cup Gourmet Mushroom's Tri-Mycogen mushroom powder or reishi mushroom powder

¼ cup schisandra berry powder

¼ cup slippery elm powder

2 tablespoons ashwaganda powder

1½ tablespoons licorice powder

¼ cup unsweetened cocoa powder

2 teaspoons vanilla extract

Extra shredded coconut for rolling

Spice Versions

1 tablespoon ground ginger and 1 teaspoon ground cinnamon

~ or ~

2 teaspoon ground cinnamon, ¾ teaspoon ground nutmeg and ¼ teaspoon ground cloves

~ or ~

2 teaspoon ground cardamom and 1 teaspoon ground cinnamon

1. Place the almonds, coconut oil and honey in a food processor and process until it is creamy. Put in a large bowl.
2. Add the coconut, powdered herbs, unsweetened cocoa powder and whatever blend of spices you choose. Use your hands to mix everything evenly.
3. Roll into balls using a level tablespoon of the mixture for each one, and then roll the balls in shredded coconut.

Makes 40 – 45 truffles

Nettle & Seaweed Spice Blend

1 cup dried nettles

1 cup dried basil

⅓ cup sesame seeds

⅓ cup pumpkin seeds

⅓ cup chia seeds

1½ tablespoons sunflower seeds

2½ tablespoons dried dandelion leaf

2½ tablespoons milk thistle seed

2 tablespoons powdered or granulated garlic

1 tablespoon dried thyme

2 teaspoons turmeric

½ tablespoon black pepper

½ – 1 teaspoon cayenne

½ ounce powdered sea vegetables such as nori, wakame, dulse or kelp

1. Grind the dried herbs and seeds separately using a spice grinder.
2. Whisk all the ingredients together in a large bowl to combine everything evenly.
3. Fill a small spice jar and place on your kitchen table where you will see and use it. Store the rest in a glass jar in the refrigerator.

Makes 2 – 2½ cups

Tips

• See the Resource Guide for sources of high quality herbs and sea vegetables.

• Use Nettle & Seaweed Spice Blend instead of salt to add flavor and nutrients to all your food.

Thanks to Gail Julian at the California School of Herbal Studies for this wonderful recipe.

Gomasio

Gomasio is a flavorful nutritional powerhouse. Used as a replacement for plain table salt, it's a delicious way to reduce sodium while adding a little calcium, magnesium, iron, protein, and fiber to your diet.

¼ cup raw organic sesame seeds, any color

1 teaspoon sea salt

1 – 2 teaspoons dulse or nori flakes or powder (optional)

½ teaspoon dried garlic (optional)

1. Place the seeds in a dry, heavy-bottomed frying pan and toast on very low heat, stirring often, until the seeds are golden and start to pop. Remove to a small bowl. The longer and slower the cooking, the more intense the flavor will be. On a low flame, the seeds may take as long as 20 minutes to toast.
2. Cool the seeds for at least 10 minutes, then grind them with the sea salt (and dulse if you are using it) in a spice grinder, just until some of the seeds have cracked. Gomasio should have some texture.
3. Store in a small jar and use on salads, grains, steamed vegetables or any other foods you choose.

Makes ¼ cup

Appendix • Resource Guide

CONTENTS

There are many books, cookbooks, companies
and websites available to support a healthy lifestyle.
Here are a few to inspire your journey.

Nutrition

General Nutrition

Diet and Nutrition: A Holistic Approach, Rudolph Ballentine, MD, The Himalayan International Institute of Yoga Science and Philosophy of the U.S.A, 1978

Digestive Wellness, Liz Lipski, McGraw-Hill, 2005

The Encyclopedia of Healing Foods, Michael T. Murray, Joseph Pizzorno, Atria Books, 2005

Enzyme Nutrition, Edward Howell, Avery, 1985

Radical Healing: Integrating the World's Great Therapeutic Traditions to Create a New Transformative Medicine, Rudolph Ballentine, MD, Three River's Press, 2000

The Safe Shopper's Bible: A Consumer's Guide to Nontoxic Household Products, Cosmetics and Food, David Steinman, Samuel S. Epstein, Wiley Publishing, 1995

The Spectrum: A Scientifically Proven Program to Feel Better, Live Longer, Lose Weight and Gain Health, Dr. Dean Ornish, Ballantine Books, 2007

What to Eat, Marion Nestle, North Point Press, 2007

Nutrition & Cancer – Books and Websites

Foods to Fight Cancer: Essential Foods to Help Prevent Cancer, Richard Beliveau and Denis Gingras, DK Adult, 2007

Nature's Cancer Fighting Foods, Verne Varne, Penguin Putnam, 2001

www.aicr.org - American Institute for Cancer Research is the cancer charity that fosters research on diet and cancer prevention, interprets the evidence, and educates the public about the results.

www.dietandcancerreport.org - Expert reports from the World Cancer Research Fund and American Institute for Cancer Research on *Food, Nutrition, Physical Activity and the Prevention of Cancer: A Global Perspective,* as well as the companion report, *Policy and Action for Cancer Prevention.* Website provides the most up to date reference and resource materials associated with both reports.

Heart Health

Dr. Dean Ornish's Program for Reversing Heart Disease, Dr. Dean Ornish, Ivy Books, December, 1995

Reversing Heart Disease: A Vital New Program to Help Prevent, Treat, and Eliminate Cardiac Problems without Surgery, Julian M. Whitaker, M.D., Warner Books, Inc. 2002

Stress, Diet and Your Heart: A Lifetime Program for Healing Your Heart Without Drugs or Surgery, Dr. Dean Ornish, First Signet Printing, 1984

The Sinatra Solution, Metabolic Cardiology, Stephen T. Sinatra, M.D., F.A.C.C., Basic Health Publications, Inc., 2005

Cookbooks

General Whole Foods

Clean Food: A Seasonal Guide to Eating Close to the Source with More than 200 Recipes for a More Sustainable You, Terry Walters, Sterling Epicure, 2009

Farmer John's Cookbook: The Real Dirt on Vegetables, Farmer John Peterson and Angelic Organics, Gibbs Smith, Publisher, 2006

Healing with Whole Foods: Asian Traditions and Modern Nutrition, Paul Pitchford, North Atlantic Books, 2002

Nourishing Traditions, Sally Fallon, New Trends Publishing, Inc., 2001

Specialty Cookbooks

Sea Vegetable Celebration, Shep Erhart & Leslie Cerier, Book Publishing Company, 2001

Sprouts: The Miracle Food, Steve Meyerowitz, Book Publishing Co., 1999 www.sproutman.com

Stevia Sweet Recipes, Jeffrey Goettemoeller, Square One Publishers, 1998

Wild Fermentation, Sandor Ellix Katz, Chelsea Green Publishing, 2003

Sprouting/Raw Foods Cookbooks

Conscious Eating, Gabriel Cousens, M.D., North Atlantic Books and Essene Vision Books, 2000

Rainbow Green Live-Food Cuisine, Gabriel Coursens, M.D., North Atlantic Books and Essene Vision Books, 2003

The Complete Book of Raw Food, Julie Rodwell, Victoria Boutenko, Juliano Brotman, and Nomi Shannon, Hatherleigh Press, August 2008

Cancer Specific Cookbooks

The Cancer-Fighting Cookbook, Rebecca Katz, Random House, 2009

Cooking with Foods that Fight Cancer, Richard Beliveau, Denis Gingras, McClelland & Stewart, 2007

One Bite at a Time: Nourishing Recipes for Cancer Survivors and their Families, Rebecca Katz, Celestial Arts Press, 2008

The What to Eat if you Have Cancer Cookbook (Revised): Healing Foods that Boost Your Immune System, Daniella Chace and Maureen Keane, McGraw Hill, 2006

Diabetes Specific Cookbooks

Diabetes & Heart Healthy Cookbook, Published by: the American Heart Association and the American Diabetes Association

There Is a Cure for Diabetes, Gabriel Cousins, M.D., North Atlantic Books, 2008

Heart Health Cookbooks

The Healthy Heart Cookbook: Over 700 Recipes for Every Day and Every Occasion, Joseph C. Piscatella and Bernie Piscatella, Black Dog and Leventhal Publishers, 2004

Herbal Information

Adaptogens: Herbs for Strength, Stamina & Stress Relief, David Winston & Steven Maimes, Healing Arts Press, 2007

Breast Cancer? Breast Health! The Wise Woman Way, Susan Weed, Ash Tree Publishing, 1996

Herbal Medicine, Healing & Cancer, Donald Yance, Keats Publishing, 1999

Holistic Herbal: A Safe and Practical Guide to Making and Using Herbal Remedies, David Hoffman, 2003

Integrative & Alternative Medicine

Anticancer: A New Way of Life, David Servan-Schreiber, Viking, 2008

Choices in Healing: Integrating the Best of Conventional and Complementary Approaches to Cancer, Michael Lerner, MIT Press, 1996

The Healing Secrets of Food by Deborah Kesten, New World Library, Novato, California, 2001

Integrative Oncology, Donald Abrams, Andrew Weil, Oxford University Press, 2009

Life over Cancer: The Block Center Program for Integrative Cancer Treatment, Keith Block, Bantam Dell, 2009

Mind-Body Unity: A New Vision for Mind-Body Science and Medicine, Henry Dreher, The Johns Hopkins University Press, 2003

www.cancerdecisions.com - Website created by Ralph Moss, Ph.D., a leading author and consultant on cancer treatment. *The Moss Reports* provide detailed yet readable explanations for each type of cancer diagnosis. Each report contains Moss's recommendations of the most successful treatments in North America and Europe, as well as innovative therapies offered at cancer centers.

www.blockmd.com - Block Center for Integrative Cancer Treatment - Founded nearly 30 years ago, the Block Center is one of the leading integrative cancer treatment facilities.

www.ewg.org - Environmental Working Group – Information about organic food and products that are green and chemical free.

www.innovativehealing.com - Nutrition information and teleseminars on health and nutrition by Liz Lipski, Ph.D., CCN.

www.westonprice.org - Weston Price Foundation - The Foundation is dedicated to restoring nutrient-dense foods to the human diet through education, research and activism. It supports a number of movements that contribute to this objective including accurate nutrition instruction, organic and biodynamic farming, pasture-feeding of livestock, community-supported farms, honest and informative labeling, prepared parenting and nurturing therapies.

Local Food, Ecology & Sustainability

There are hundreds of wonderful books covering these topics. The ones that follow are simply a selection of those that have crossed our paths and most influenced our thinking.

Animal, Vegetable, Miracle: A Year of Food Life, Barbara Kingsolver, Harper Collins, 2007

Deep Economy: the Wealth of Communities and the Durable Future, Bill McKibben, Times Books, Henry Holt and Company, LLC, 2007

The Earth Knows My Name: Food, Culture and Sustainability in the Gardens of Ethnic Americans, Patricia Klindienst, Beacon Press, 2006

The Earth Moved, Amy Stewart, Algonquin Books of Chapel Hill, 2004

Eat Here, Brian Halwell, W.W. Norton & Company, 2004

Enough: Why the World's Poorest Starve in an Age of Plenty, Roger Thurow and Scott Kilman, Public Affairs Books, 2009

Fields of Plenty: A Farmer's Journey in Search of Real Food and the People Who Grow It, Michael Abelman, Chronicle Books, 2005

Full Moon Feast: Food and the Hunger for Connection, Jessica Prentice, Chelsea Green Publishing, 2006

Hope's Edge, Frances Moore Lappe and Anna Lappe, Jeremy P. Tarcher/Putnam, 2002

In Defense of Food: An Eater's Manifesto, Michael Pollan, The Penguin Press, 2008

The Lost Language of Plants, Stephen Harrod Buhner, Chelsea Green, 2002

Paradox of Plenty, Harvey Levenstein, University of California Press, 2003

The Way We Eat: Why Our Food Choices Matter, Peter Singer and Jim Mason, Rodale Books, 2006

High Quality Ingredients

Herbs

Mountain Rose Herbs - Based in Eugene, Oregon, Mountain Rose sells the highest quality sustainably grown herbs in quantities as small as 4 ounces. - www.mountainroseherbs.com

Starwest Botanicals – An on-line source of high quality dried organic herbs, bulk spices, loose leaf organic teas, organic essential oils and aromatherapy supplies since 1975. The company is based in Sacramento, California. - www.starwest-botanicals.com

Local, Organic Food

Local Harvest - The best organic food is what's grown closest to you. Use Local Harvest's website to find farmers' markets, family farms, and other local sources of sustainably grown food such as grass-fed beef and organic eggs. - www.localharvest.org

Sea Vegetables

Mendocino Sea Vegetable Company - Since 1980 Mendocino Sea Vegetable Company has been providing quality wildcrafted sea vegetables and information. - www.seaweed.net

Maine Coast Sea Vegetables – Quality supplier of sustainably harvested sea vegetables on the east coast. Web site includes recipes and educational information. – www.seaveg.com

Mushrooms & Mushroom Powders

Gourmet Mushrooms offers fresh and dried mushrooms, nutraceutical mushroom powders including Trimyco-Gen which The Ceres Community Project uses in our Vitality Truffles, and mushroom growing kits.
- www.gmushrooms.com

Green Superfoods

Healthforce Nutritionals - HealthForce realizes that certain nutritional supplements can and do make a dramatic difference in one's state of health, or lack thereof. They sell Vitamineral Green Superfoods, herbs and products for cleansing.
- www.healthforce.com

Hemp Foods and Oils

Manitoba Harvest Hemp Foods – High quality hemp seeds, protein powders, hemp oil and hemp nut butter.
- www.manitobaharvest.com

Wild Seafood and Organics

Vital Choice - This company's products are recognized for their health benefits, purity, quality and are sustainably harvested from healthy, well-managed fisheries. They do not sell factory-farmed salmon or any other foods that fail to meet their safe and high environmental standards. - www.vitalchoice.com

Support Services

Support Services for Living with Cancer

www.cancercare.org - Non-profit organization that provides free, professional support services for anyone affected by cancer.

www.canceradvocacy.org - National Coalition for Cancer Survivorship is the oldest survivor-led cancer advocacy organization in the country and a highly respected authentic voice at the federal level, advocating for quality cancer care for all Americans and empowering cancer survivors.

Commonweal Cancer Help Program

www.commonweal.org

The Commonweal Cancer Help Program (CCHP) is a week-long retreat for people with cancer. The goal is to help participants live better and, where possible, longer lives. The Cancer Help Program addresses the unmet needs of people with cancer. These include finding balanced information on choices in healing, mainstream and complementary therapies; exploring emotional and spiritual dimensions of cancer; discovering that illness can sometimes lead to a richer and fuller life; and experiencing genuine community with others facing a cancer diagnosis.

Smith Farm Center

www.smithfarm.com - Smith Farm Center for Healing and the Arts is a nonprofit health, education and creative arts organization that serves individuals, families and communities affected by cancer and other serious illnesses in the Washington, DC area.

Block Center for Integrative Cancer Care

www.blockmd.com

www.lifeovercancer.com

Founded nearly 30 years ago, the Block Center is one of the leading integrative cancer treatment facilities.

BioMed Clinic for Oncology

Tischberger, Street 5-8
Bad Bergzabern, Germany
412-623-4716

Dr. Dieter Hager, MD, PhD, DSc

Integrative oncology center offering technologies for treating cancer not available in the United States.

Cancer Treatment Centers of America (CTCA)

13200 West Fillmore Street
Goodyear, AZ 85338

www.cancercenter.com

Cancer Treatment Centers of America (CTCA) offers patients the most sophisticated forms of surgery, radiation therapy and chemotherapy in combination with complementary medicine therapies, including nutrition therapy, naturopathic medicine, mind-body medicine, and spiritual support.

Society for Integrative Oncology

www.integrativeonc.org - Society for Integrative Oncology - The Society for Integrative Oncology (SIO) is a non-profit, multidisciplinary organization founded in 2003 for health professionals committed to the study and application of complementary therapies and botanicals for cancer patients. It provides a convenient forum for presentation, discussion and peer review of evidence-based research and treatment modalities in the discipline known as integrative medicine. It makes a clear distinction between "alternative" or unproven and "complementary" or tested useful therapies in cancer care.

The Wellness Community

www.thewellnesscommunity.org - Non-profit organization dedicated to providing free emotional support, education and hope for people with cancer and their loved ones.

Support services for Heart Health

www.americanheart.org - American Heart Association- Dedicated to providing you with education and information on fighting heart disease.

http://www.mendedhearts.org - Mended Hearts - Hope for recovery. Hope for a rich, full life. For more than 50 years, Mended Hearts has been offering the gift of hope and encouragement to heart patients, their families and caregivers. Patients, spouses, family members, friends, medical professionals, Mended Hearts brings together all of us who are faced with the realities of heart disease to form a network of caring individuals.

www.mayoclinic.com - Mayo Clinic - Provides valuable information on the causes of heart disease, preventing heart disease, and treatments.

Support services for Diabetes

www.diabetessociety.org - Diabetes Society – Offers diabetes education and support and serves 20,000 people annually, giving education, hope, and encouragement to those living with diabetes. Programs include an ADA recognized diabetes self-management education program, community-wide diabetes screenings, support groups, and diabetes education camps for children, teenagers, and families. The Society also helps recruit participants for the latest state of the art diabetes clinical trials.

Registered nurses, registered dietitians and certified diabetes educators provide clients with the latest information about medications, supplies and blood glucose management. The goal is to teach people with diabetes how to live healthy lives and avoid the often devastating severe complications of the disease.

www.diabetes.org - American Diabetes Association - The American Diabetes Association is leading the fight against the deadly consequences of diabetes and fighting for those affected by diabetes. The Association funds research to prevent, cure and manage diabetes; delivers services to hundreds of communities; provides objective and credible information; and gives voice to those denied their rights because of diabetes. Founded in 1940, our mission is to prevent and cure diabetes and to improve the lives of all people affected by diabetes.

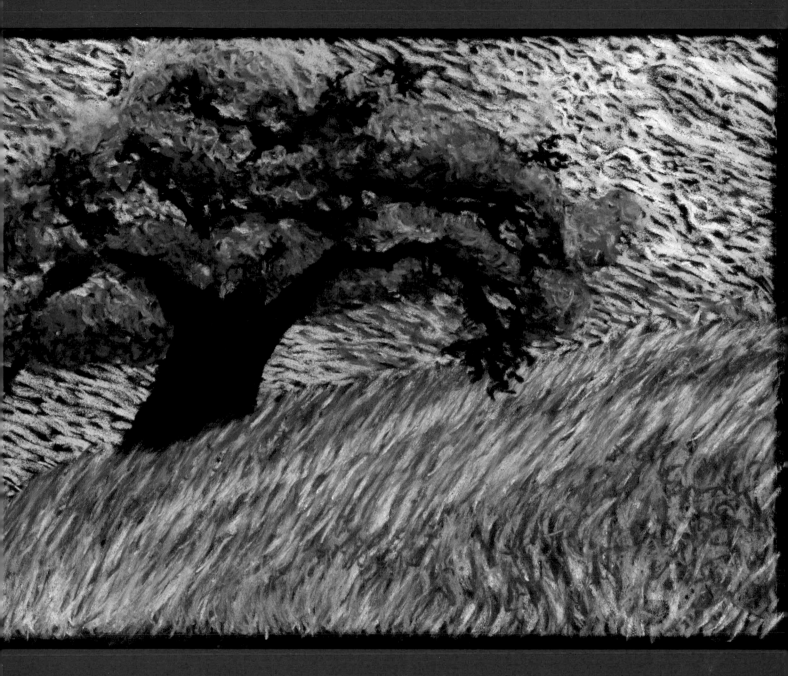

I am a mother of two teenagers, a "plein air" painter (on location landscapes), wife, community activist and a person thriving while having cancer. I was first diagnosed with breast cancer in 1996, when my children were three and five years old. Shocked when the cancer returned with a vengeance nine years later, extensively in my bones and lungs, I have continued using allopathic and integrative medicine.

It has always been clear to me that diet is an important aspect of dealing with cancer. Experiencing Cathryn's unfolding of The Ceres Community Project has been an incredible inspiration to me. Her remarkable vision has manifested into a myriad of dimensions of service and outreach, touching hundreds of people's lives, including my own. Every mouthful is filled with loving kindness and generosity!

~ *Nancy Rosser Hutchins*

Organic Grocery List

Vegetables
Artichokes
Asparagus
Beets
Bok choy
Broccoli
Burdock
Cabbage
Carrots
Celery
Chard
Corn
Diakon / Radish
Fennel
Garlic
Ginger
Jicama
Kohl Rabi
Kale
Lettuce
Mixed salad greens
Onions
Leeks
Parsley
Potatoes
Peas
Spinach
Squash
String beans
Sweet potatoes
Tangerine
Tomatoes
Turnips
Winter squash

Fruit
Apples
Avocado
Bananas
Berries
Cherries
Lemon
Oranges
Papaya
Pear
Satsuma
Watermelon

Legumes
Adzuki beans
Black beans
Chickpeas
Kidney beans
Lentils
Mung beans
White beans

Eggs
Free range

Grains
Amaranth
Basamati rice
Brown rice
Buckwheat
Cornmeal
Couscous
Millet
Polenta
Oats,
    whole or rolled
Quinoa
Wild rice

Nuts/Seeds
Almonds
Brazil nuts
Cashews
Chia seeds
Coconut
Flax seeds
Hemp seeds
Pecans
Pumpkin seeds
Sesame seeds
Sunflower seeds
Walnuts

Oils
Coconut oil
Olive oil
Sesame oil
Toasted sesame oil

Dairy
Living Cultures of:
    Kefir
    Yogurt
    Sour cream
    Cottage cheese
Raw organic milk
Raw organic butter
Raw organic cheese

Poultry /Seafood
Free-range,
    organic poultry
Wild, sustainably
    harvested fish

Mushrooms
Crimini
Miatake
Porcini
Portobello
Shiitake

Dried Herbs & Spices
Black pepper
Sea salt

_____
_____
_____
_____

Fresh Herbs
Basil
Cilantro
Italian flat-leaf
 parsley
Mint

Dried Fruits
Apricots
Cherries
Cranberries
Currants
Dates
Figs
Goji berries
Raisins

Condiments
Apple cider vinegar
Balsamic vinegar
Bragg's Amino
Gomasio
Mirin
Tamari
Brown rice vinegar
Umeboshi vinegar

Canned Foods
Coconut milk
Chickpeas
Black beans
Diced tomatoes
Tomato sauce
Sardines

Beverages
Amazake grain drink
Herbal teas
Nut milk
Oat milk
Rice milk

Frozen Foods
Corn
Berries
Peas
Spinach

Sea Vegetables
Arame
Dulse flakes
Hijiki
Kombu
Nori
Wakame

Noodles
Asian rice noodles
Brown Rice Pasta
Soba noodles
Kamut or
 spelt pasta
Udon noodles
Quinoa pasta

Flour
Barley flour
Brown rice flour
Corn meal
Spelt flour
Tapioca flour
Quinoa flour
Whole wheat
 pastry flour

Sweeteners
Brown rice syrup
Maple syrup
Molasses
Raw Honey
Stevia

Misc.
Bee pollen
Green powder
Lecithin
Mochi
Tempeh
Whey or rice
 protein powder

colophon

typefaces
Gill Sans for the heads
Clearface for the text

software
Adobe InDesign CS4
Adobe Photoshop CS4
Adobe Illustrator CS4
Adobe Acrobat 9 Pro
Microsoft Word (various versions)

hardware
iMac
   3 GHz Intel Core 2 Duo
   4 GB RAM
   24 inch display
   1 TB hard drive
Xerox Phaser 6280DN
Canon MP830
Canon 10D
Canon Rebel

music
Swan Lake - Svetlanov, USSR State Symphony Orchestra
Fishbear THEEP - www.FishbearMusic.com
The Best of Bond...James Bond
Bruce Springsteen
Taylor Swift
Frank Sinatra
Madeleine Peyroux
Fleetwood Mac
Willie Nelson
Elvis Presley
Dire Straits